The British Isles through Geological Time

A northward drift

J. P. B. LOVELL

Lecturer in Geology, University of Edinburgh

London
GEORGE ALLEN & UNWIN
Boston   Sydney

First published in 1977
Second impression 1978

© George Allen & Unwin (Publishers) Ltd, 1977

ISBN 0 04 554003 9

Printed Offset Litho in Great Britain by
Cox & Wyman Ltd
London, Fakenham and Reading

CONTENTS

ACKNOWLEDGEMENTS

This project had its roots in discussions with my colleague Dr T. P. Scoffin about the best way to teach a short course on the geological history of the British Isles to first-year students at Edinburgh University with little or no background in geology. I am most grateful to Dr Scoffin for his great help in the early stages of this work, during which we were assisted by Mr G. O. Gibb and his colleagues of Audio-Visual Services, University of Edinburgh.

Professor G. Kelling, Mr J. A. G. Thomas, Mr D. B. Thompson, Professor E. K. Walton and Dr R. C. L. Wilson made many helpful comments on my early proposals about the form of the book. Mr Thomas and Dr Wilson made further detailed comments on an early draft and I am most grateful to them.

At a critical stage the enthusiasm and wise advice of Professor P. Allen led to the production of a much revised final draft. Valuable comments on various sections of this final draft were made by Dr W. E. A. Phillips (Precambrian), Dr J. W. Cowie (Cambrian), Professor H. B. Whittington (Ordovician), Professor G. Y. Craig (Silurian), Dr P. F. Friend (Devonian), Dr W. H. C. Ramsbottom (Carboniferous), Mr D. B. Thompson (Permian and Triassic), Dr A. Hallam and Dr B. W. Sellwood (Jurassic), Dr J. M. Hancock (Cretaceous), Dr A. C. Dunham (Tertiary), Dr J. B. Sissons (Quaternary), Mr F. G. Dimes (economic geology) and Dr R. A. Scrutton (other sections). Professor G. F. Mitchell gave advice on the latest readvance of the ice sheets in Ireland. Professor J. R. L. Allen gave advice on the style of the maps.

It is perhaps more important than usual in the case of this book to claim that the author alone is responsible for its shortcomings; no doubt the reader will be quick to identify places where I have persisted in error in spite of the wealth of distinguished advice I have received.

Throughout, I have had the very great benefit of many discussions with my colleagues in Edinburgh, both staff and students. I particularly thank Professor Gordon Craig for his encouragement and help. Mr Roger Jones of George Allen & Unwin has been closely involved with the production of this book, and I am specially grateful to him. Mr Brian Johnston has drafted the maps and has made many valuable suggestions; he has been a key figure in the production of the book. Mrs Ann Brackenridge, Mrs Janette Brunton and Mrs Jeanette Ferguson typed the many versions of the text without ever confessing boredom.

Finally, I thank James, David and Heather Lovell for making sure that I was awake early each day to start work on the book, and Caroline Lovell for creating enough peace for me to complete that work.

SOURCES

The works cited under 'Reading' have provided much of the material. A book like this is based even more than most on the work of fellow geologists, past and present. Though I have seen in the field a fair amount of the evidence used in this book, I have collected only the tiniest part of it myself. Without wishing in any way to transfer the blame for the shortcomings of the book to my mentors, I want to thank those who have offered me in lectures and other ways their own ideas on the geological development of the British Isles. I specially thank Drs W. S. McKerrow, H. G. Reading and the late K. S. Sandford and Professors J. Haller, B. Kummel, R. Siever and H. B. Whittington. Those I have thanked elsewhere for their help during the preparation of the book have also provided much invaluable additional material.

The various positions of the British Isles through time depicted in the section on 'Geological time' are redrawn from 'Phanerozoic world maps' by A. G. Smith, J. C. Briden and G. E. Drewry, pp. 1–42 in *Special papers in palaeontology*, no. 12: *Organisms and continents through time*, editor N. F. Hughes, published by the Palaeontological Association, London in 1973. The Carboniferous positions are modified by the results reported by P. Turner and D. H. Tarling in 1975 in *Journal of the Geological Society of London*, **131**, 469–88.

The dates quoted for each period are based on the paper 'The pre-Pleistocene Phanerozoic time-scale – a review' by R. St J. Lambert, pp. 9–31 in *The Phanerozoic time-scale – a supplement*: Special publication no. 5 of the Geological Society of London (1971), with some reference to the original (1964) Geological Society publication *The Phanerozoic time-scale*, edited by W. B. Harland, A. G. Smith and B. Wilcock.

The information about offshore geology comes largely from *Petroleum and the continental shelf of north-west Europe*, Volume 1, *Geology*, edited by A. W. Woodland and published by Applied Science Publishers in 1975.

The possible late Precambrian relationship of north-west Scotland and Greenland, shown on the palaeogeographical map for that time, is redrawn from Figure 10 in G. E. Williams' (1969) paper 'Petrography and origin of pebbles from Torridonian strata (late Precambrian), north-west Scotland', pp. 609–29 in *North Atlantic—geology and continental drift*, Memoir 12 of the American Association of Petroleum Geologists, edited by G. M. Kay.

The data on limits of evaporite deposits in Yorkshire shown in the Permian outcrop map are summarised from Figure 74 of D. B. Smith's chapter 'Evaporites' in *The geology and mineral resources of Yorkshire*, edited by D. H. Rayner and J. E. Hemingway and published by the Yorkshire Geological Society in 1974.

The outcrop map of the British Isles and the adjacent continental shelf is based largely on the map published in 1972 by the Institute of Geological Sciences, *The sub-Pleistocene geology of the British Isles and the adjacent continental shelf*. Additional information comes from recent work by, among others, P. E. Binns, M. H. P. Bott, D. Curry, R. McQuillin and A. J. Smith.

The map accompanying the summary of tectonic and igneous activity is based largely on the map published in 1966 by the Institute of Geological Sciences, *Tectonic map of Great Britain and Northern Ireland*.

INTRODUCTION

This book is for the beginner who wishes to know the broad outlines of the geological evolution of the British Isles. Little previous knowledge of geology is assumed. I hope it is useful to those taking a first course in geology, during which they are necessarily introduced to much additional supporting material.

The palaeogeographical maps are reconstructions of the geography at specific points in geological time; they should be considered as photographs of a continually changing landscape, taken at long intervals, as individual frames on a moving film. Inevitably, such palaeogeographical maps give an impression of continuity during the main periods of geological time, followed by rapid and substantial changes before the next period begins. This is of course a false impression, but even if I were to show several maps for each period (two have been used for the Carboniferous and two for the Cretaceous), these would still imply discontinuities that simply do not exist. The text tries to remedy this by stressing the time involved in each period, and the gradation of palaeogeography from one (man-defined) period to the next, but the only real cure is to develop a sense of geological time. An attempt has been made to show in the section on 'Geological time' the effort of imagination needed; the only sure way is to study geology over a long time yourself, especially in the field.

I cannot emphasise enough the importance of fieldwork in all respects. It is the ultimate source of the many facts and interpretations that have led scores of geologists to the type of conclusions attempted here. To understand the basis of this book properly the reader must do at least some fieldwork. The reading suggested below becomes very much more enjoyable and useful when you have carried out some work on rocks yourself and such work is within the reach of any beginner, especially if helped by a more experienced teacher.

The present-day outline of the British Isles, areas of outcrop, a scale and an indication of the direction of north, have not been added to the palaeogeographical maps. I have found that the presence of these curbs the imagination. In class I sketch palaeogeography on to the transparent roll of an overhead projector, above a transparency bearing an outline map of the present-day British Isles with outcrops, and then remove the transparency with the outline outcrop map. I have found this a useful way to guide students away from thinking of palaeogeography in too restricted a fashion. Because it is not possible to arrange such superimposition of the maps in this book, I have added a grid to both outcrop and palaeogeographical maps so that reference may be made from one to the other. Such reference must be made with caution; it will become clear to the reader that the present outcrops of the rocks shown on the maps form areas of different sizes, shapes and even different relative positions from the areas covered by the rocks when they were originally laid down, because of both deformation and later burial and erosion.

Attention has been drawn in the text only to those fossils that are important in British stratigraphy. They may be important because they are abundant, because they are specially useful in correlation or because they have particular environmental significance; some really useful fossils may be all three of these things.

Various geological terms are printed in bold type and defined where they first appear; their place of first appearance is recorded in the index. *The Penguin dictionary of geology* by D. G. A. Whitten and J. R. V. Brooks is helpful with further reading.

This book is not a mine of information. It is designed to give a framework for further reading and thinking; its maps are designed to be traced, overlain with others, added to and modified. To help with this I suggest some reading to support the various sections of the text.

READING

Fossils
British fossils (Palaeozoic, Mesozoic, Caenozoic), published by the British Museum (Natural History) in three volumes, is beautifully illustrated and includes much information on British stratigraphy. *The history of life* by A. L. McAlester (Prentice-Hall) is a good introduction to palaeontology.

Areas of outcrop and palaeogeography
The data on outcrop areas shown here come primarily from maps published by the Institute of Geological Sciences (formerly the Geological Survey of Great Britain). The '25-mile' map gives the whole picture on one sheet, the 'Ten-mile' map (two sheets) is especially useful for long road and rail journeys, and the 1:63 360 and new 1:50 000 series are good for local work. *The British regional geology* series (H.M.S.O.) and the guides published by the Geologists' Association and other societies give local details and interpretations.

British stratigraphy by F. A. Middlemiss (George Allen & Unwin) and *Historical geology* (Open University Press, S23: Block 6) are introductory texts, while *Stratigraphy of the British Isles* by D. H. Rayner (Cambridge University Press) and *The geological history of the British Isles* by G. M. Bennison and A. E. Wright (Edward Arnold) go into more detail. The Open University book deals with plate tectonics (large scale movements of continents and oceans) in relation to the stratigraphy of the British Isles, as does *The geological evolution of the British Isles* by T. R. Owen (Pergamon Press). *A palaeogeographical atlas of the British Isles and adjacent parts of Europe* by L. J. Wills (Blackie and Son) is a classic. *The geological column* (Manchester Museum) provides a very useful coloured fold-out summary of the stratigraphy of the British Isles. *Geologic time* by D. L. Eicher (Prentice-Hall) is an excellent introduction to stratigraphical principles.

Continental drift and plate tectonics
The story of the Earth (Geological Museum, H.M.S.O.) is a well illustrated simple introduction. *Planet Earth* and *Continents Adrift*, both collections of readings from Scientific American (Freeman), provide useful introductions. *A revolution in the Earth sciences: from continental drift to plate tectonics* by A. Hallam (Oxford University Press) is a lucid account of the historical developments involved. 'The plain man's guide to plate tectonics' by E. R. Oxburgh, published in volume 85 of the *Proceedings of the Geologists' Association* (pp. 299–357, 1974) is a good introductory article for those with some background in geology.

Economic
Earth resources by B. J. Skinner (Prentice-Hall) is a good introduction to economic geology. *The British regional geology* series (see above) covers some economic aspects, while the Open University's *The Earth's physical resources* (S26: Blocks 1 to 6) gives an introduction to the subject and refers to many examples from the British Isles. *The politics of physical resources* edited by P. J. Smith (Open University Press) is recommended.

CONTINENTAL DRIFT AND PLATE TECTONICS

The different latitudes of the British Isles at times in the past, shown in the Figure in the section on 'Geological time', have been determined from **palaeomagnetic** evidence. This evidence comes from certain iron-bearing minerals, especially those found in ancient flows of **magma** (molten rock) from volcanoes. These minerals may retain for many millions of years magnetic information concerning the position of the north and south poles at the time the magmas were erupted; the information was 'frozen' into the rocks as the magmas cooled, crystals formed and the rocks solidified. This palaeomagnetic work can indicate palaeolatitude but cannot reveal palaeolongitude; the relative longitudinal positions of the British Isles shown on the Figure are arbitrary.

Why did the position of the British Isles change? And why is the northwestern part of the present British Isles shown as being separate from the rest of the British Isles during the early Palaeozoic?

The British Isles are not alone in having moved great distances over the Earth's surface in the past; much evidence from different parts of the world points to widespread **continental drift**. Until recently many geologists were describing rather than interpreting this movement, if indeed they believed in it at all. A new hypothesis has been put forward and widely accepted in the last few years, the notion of **plate tectonics**. The idea of plate tectonics is founded on studies of processes operating on the present-day Earth. The fundamental principles are simple, though their application to the geological record is not so simple.

The Earth has a quite rigid outer skin, about a hundred kilometres thick, which is divided into a small number of large **plates**. These plates move relative to each other, and it is their **margins** that are of special geological importance. There are three main types of margin:

1. **Constructive**, where **basalt**, a silica-poor igneous rock, is added at cracks to the plate margin, as magma rises up from hotter regions below as the plates spread apart. This process causes uplift of the plate margin to form mountains, which may be submarine. Small earthquakes are associated with the igneous activity. An example of a constructive plate margin is the submarine mountain range called the Mid-Atlantic Ridge.
2. **Destructive**, where one plate moves under another as they converge. This process causes earthquakes, some of them large, and mountain building. It also leads to the formation of **andesites** (extrusive igneous rocks richer in silica than are basalts) and **granites** (silica-rich intrusive igneous rocks) as parts of the lower plate melt as it moves down into the heat of the Earth's interior. Examples of destructive plate margins are found around or near most of the edge of the Pacific Ocean.

3. **Conservative**, where plates slide past each other, and are neither created nor destroyed. This process may cause large earthquakes. An example of this type of margin is the San Andreas Fault in western U.S.A.

Plates move at only a few centimetres a year, or, to put the rate in more useful terms geologically, only a few tens of kilometres in a million years.

It is important to note that plate margins are not necessarily in the same place as continental margins; for example, the continental margins around the Atlantic Ocean lie within plates, not near the margins. It is possible for a continent to be split apart if a constructive margin develops in its midst, and a new ocean develops as the fragments of the continent separate. It is also possible for continents to collide at a destructive margin, as they are drawn together as intervening areas of plate covered by ocean are destroyed. The collision of India with the rest of Asia to form the Himalayas is believed to be an example of this.

What relevance does all this have to the geological evolution of the British Isles? The rocks now forming the British Isles have moved large distances in the past as parts of plates and it now seems likely that it is these plate movements that have controlled major geological events such as igneous activity and mountain building, at least since the Precambrian. It may be possible to recognise in the geological record preserved in the British Isles and elsewhere evidence for the type of plate movements involved, and it is here that the margins, of both plates and continents, have a special significance.

An attempt is made in this book to outline some of the suggested plate tectonic interpretations for each period. Such suggestions are necessarily speculative at this stage and are presented here to indicate the exciting new areas of palaeogeographical research now open to geologists. For example, it has long been known beyond reasonable doubt that mountains were formed in the present-day northern parts of the British Isles about 400 million years ago, with associated horizontal shortening of at least the upper part of the crust. It may now be possible to extend this description by invoking continental collision at a destructive plate margin.

Sedimentary rocks provide virtually all the fossils, and much of the other evidence bearing on palaeogeographical interpretation. It is useful, in the midst of the present excitement concerning plate tectonics, to recall the basic phenomena forming these rocks, those processes involved in the cycle of uplift, erosion and deposition. One of the few happy certainties in geology is that what goes up must come down; from the earliest days geologists have always had a good idea of how things come down, now they are beginning to find out how they go up.

CONSTRUCTIVE

PLAN

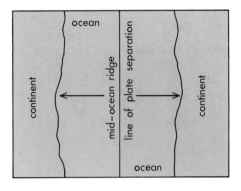

DESTRUCTIVE

PLAN

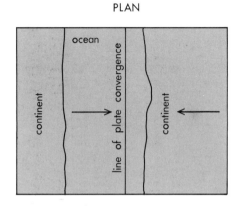

CONSERVATIVE

PLAN

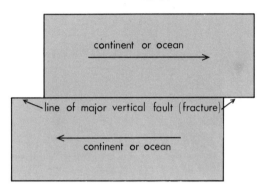

CROSS-SECTION

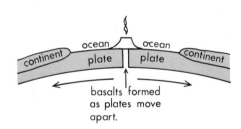

As the plates move apart the continents separate and an ocean forms between them.

CROSS-SECTION

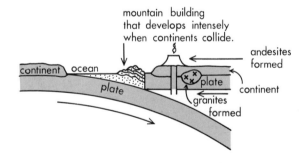

As the plates move together the ocean becomes narrower and eventually the continents collide.

MAIN TYPES OF PLATE MARGIN

KEY TO SYMBOLS USED ON MAPS

Area of **outcrop** (an area in which rocks of a given age, e.g. Cambrian, occur at the surface; these rocks may or may not be covered by soil, vegetation or other superficial features). Offshore outcrops are shown in the section 'Outcrop map of the British Isles and the adjacent continental shelf'. Intrusive igneous rocks are shown in the section 'Summary of tectonic and igneous activity'.

Delta.

Dunes of sand. Arrow indicates direction of prevailing wind.

Evaporites (salt deposits, see p. 24).

Flattening of slope, with coarser-grained sediment accumulating nearer source of sediment supply. Direction of supply of sediment indicated by arrow.

Forest.

Highlands.

Land.

Limestone reefs.

Oil and/or gas discovery offshore.

Sea.

Volcanic activity.

GEOLOGICAL TIME

To give some idea of geological time in relation to human experience, the normal time scale shown has also been compressed and equated with a calendar year. The Earth formed approximately 4600 million years ago – say at the very beginning of New Year's Day. The earliest signs of life in the fossil record are found in rocks over 3000 million years old – say the spring of the year. The approximate real time (plus or minus about 10%) and 'compressed' time are given for each former position of the British Isles shown. On the compressed scale the last glaciers disappeared from the British Isles at about 11.59 p.m. on 31 December, Jesus Christ lived and died about 14 seconds before the end of the year, the first test match was played less than a second before midnight, and our own lives represent only a fraction of the last second of the year.

Though there is still some discussion about the details of the divisions of geological time and their dating, there is general agreement concerning the main outlines.

Much early geological work was carried out in the British Isles. The names of several of the periods of geological time reflect this; they are based on British localities that serve as **type** (reference) **areas**.

The evidence for the palaeolatitudes of the British Isles shown on the right of the figure comes from the palaeomagnetic work discussed in the previous section on 'Continental drift and plate tectonics'.

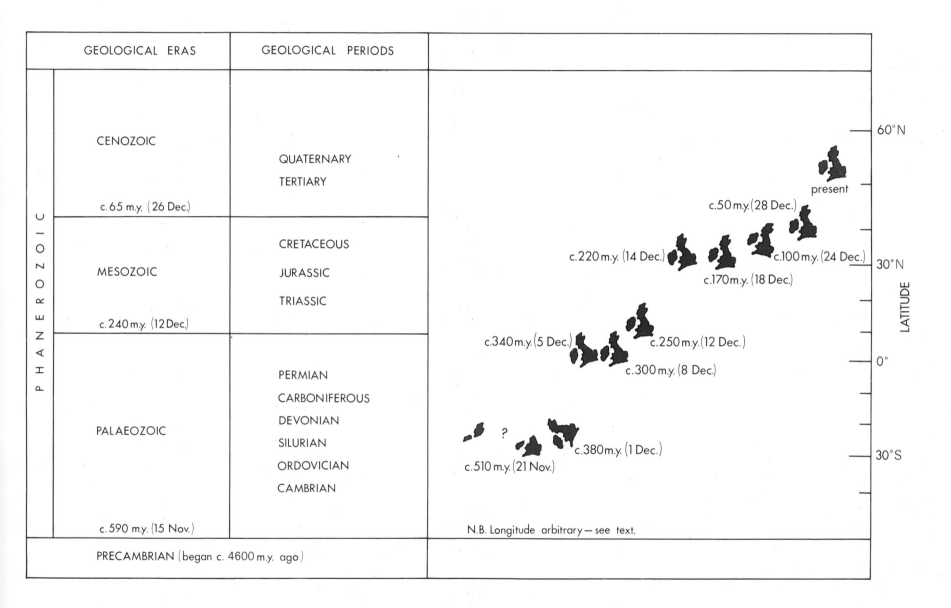

	GEOLOGICAL ERAS	GEOLOGICAL PERIODS	
P H A N E R O Z O I C	CENOZOIC c. 65 m.y. (26 Dec.)	QUATERNARY TERTIARY	
	MESOZOIC c. 240 m.y. (12 Dec.)	CRETACEOUS JURASSIC TRIASSIC	
	PALAEOZOIC c. 590 m.y. (15 Nov.)	PERMIAN CARBONIFEROUS DEVONIAN SILURIAN ORDOVICIAN CAMBRIAN	
PRECAMBRIAN (began c. 4600 m.y. ago)			

60°N

present

c.50 m.y. (28 Dec.)

c.220 m.y. (14 Dec.)

c.100 m.y. (24 Dec.)

30°N

c.170 m.y. (18 Dec.)

c.340 m.y. (5 Dec.)

c.250 m.y. (12 Dec.)

c.300 m.y. (8 Dec.)

0°

LATITUDE

?

c.380 m.y. (1 Dec.)

30°S

c.510 m.y. (21 Nov.)

N.B. Longitude arbitrary — see text.

9

PRECAMBRIAN

(about 4600 to 590 million years ago; named in relation to the succeeding period)

Fossils

Fossils are very rare, even in the youngest Precambrian. Those that are found lack hard parts, and are so primitive that they are of little use in correlation. Moreover, many Precambrian rocks have been deformed and **metamorphosed** (altered by heat and pressure) so many times and to such an extent that it would be virtually impossible to establish reliable correlations between separated areas, even if preservable organisms had been present originally. Precambrian 'stratigraphy' is, in most cases, an attempt to work out a sequence of **orogenies** (periods of deformation and mountain-building) and phases of metamorphism in a given area. This work has been helped greatly by the introduction of **radiometric dating** methods, based on measuring the products of radioactive decay in several minerals.

Areas of outcrop of special interest

North-west Scotland (Lewisian rocks)

Data: These are highly deformed, metamorphosed, varied rocks of sedimentary and igneous origin, with intrusions of **basic** (low silica content) igneous rocks. Two main phases of deformation and metamorphism are recognised with the help of radiometric dating, the first about 2600 million years ago and the second about 1800 million years ago.

Interpretation: There are insufficient data to be sure of the original environments of deposition of these rocks.

North-west Scotland (Torridonian rocks)

Data: This is a slightly deformed sequence, several thousand metres thick, mainly composed of red sandstones and **conglomerates** (sedimentary rocks that are coarser-grained than are sandstones). This sequence is **unconformable** on (that is, overlies with a break in time) the older Lewisian rocks below. A fossil soil may be found in places at the base of the Torridonian lying on the surface of the Lewisian rocks.

Interpretation: The red beds suggest, but do not prove, deposition on land; other features of the rocks indicate that they were in part laid down by rivers on older Lewisian rocks. Soils formed contemporaneously indicate a warm, moderately humid climate, possibly with dry periods or a dry season.

Highlands of Scotland (Moinian rocks)

Data: This is a much deformed sequence of metamorphosed sedimentary rocks, several thousand metres thick. Radiometric and other evidence indicates that the Moinian is older than the Torridonian, and that the Torridonian is older than the Dalradian.

Interpretation: The rocks are perhaps largely of marine origin and were deposited in varying depths of water.

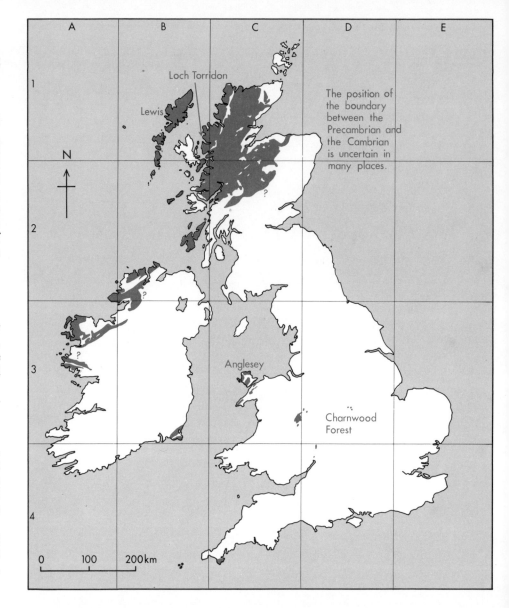

The position of the boundary between the Precambrian and the Cambrian is uncertain in many places.

Highlands of Scotland (Dalradian rocks)

Data: This is a much deformed sequence of metamorphosed sedimentary rocks, several thousand metres thick. Part of the sequence includes distinctive boulder beds. Marine Cambrian and Ordovician fossils are found in the upper part of the sequence, which is discussed in the appropriate sections.

Interpretation: The rocks were deposited in a marine environment, in which

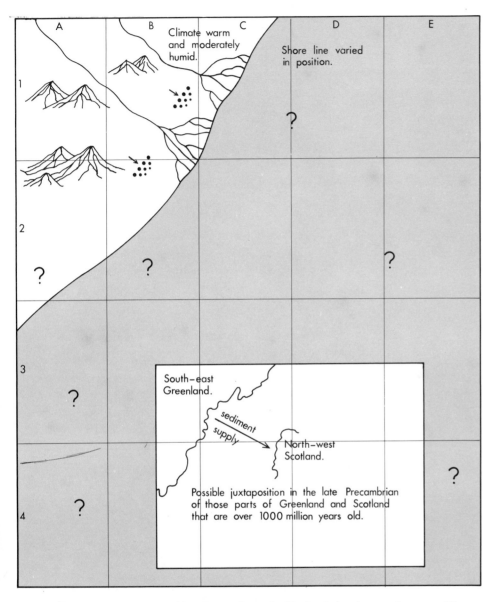

Climate warm and moderately humid.

Shore line varied in position.

South-east Greenland.

sediment supply

North-west Scotland.

Possible juxtaposition in the late Precambrian of those parts of Greenland and Scotland that are over 1000 million years old.

the depth of water probably changed markedly both in time and space. The boulder beds indicate a late Precambrian glaciation, which from evidence elsewhere appears to have been world-wide.

Wales (Anglesey and adjacent areas)

Data: Several thousand metres thickness of metamorphosed sedimentary and igneous rocks forms a sequence apparently complicated by both contemporary

and later deformation. The sedimentary rocks include limestones, sandstones and mudstones. Radiometric and other evidence indicates a late Precambrian age for the sequence.

Interpretation: These rocks formed in a variety of environments. At least some of the environments were marine, and some were tectonically unstable. The deposition of the sedimentary rocks was affected by contemporaneous igneous activity.

North and west Ireland

Data: An older sequence of much deformed and metamorphosed sedimentary rocks that resembles the Moinian of Scotland is overlain by a thick sequence, also of much deformed and metamorphosed sedimentary rocks, that is similar to the Dalradian of Scotland.

Interpretation: The rocks are perhaps largely of marine origin and were deposited in varying depths of water.

Palaeogeography

The palaeogeographical map necessarily shows only part of the area of the British Isles during only part of Precambrian time, that is, the time of deposition of the Torridonian rocks. The Torridonian was deposited mainly on land, by rivers draining highlands that lay to the north-west (present-day direction). To the south-east the land was bordered by a sea of unknown extent. The area seems to have been quite **tectonically stable** (few earth movements). Radiometric dating of the pebbles in the conglomerates, and their composition, both support the idea of a source of sediment in some of the early Precambrian rocks of what is now southern Greenland; the implications of this are discussed below and illustrated in the inset figure on the palaeogeographical map.

Continental drift and plate tectonics

It is hard to be confident about extending plate tectonic interpretation into much of the Precambrian, but in the late Precambrian rocks of Anglesey and other parts of north Wales the volume and type of igneous and sedimentary rocks, taken with the evidence for metamorphism at high pressures and the extensive zones of disturbance in the sequence, may indicate a destructive plate margin. Elsewhere there is evidence concerning much later events; it is notable that rocks closely resembling the Lewisian in type and age are now found in widely separated areas bordering the North Atlantic Ocean such as Labrador and Greenland, and that the composition of some of the rock fragments in the Torridonian sedimentary rocks suggests that they were eroded from a then adjacent Greenland. There is a clear indication here of a later separation of Greenland from north-west Scotland (see the Tertiary section).

Economic

Lewisian and Torridonian rocks provide local building materials. Precambrian rocks in Anglesey and Charnwood Forest, Leicestershire, are quarried; the latter area is an important source of igneous and metamorphic rock, suitable for use as roadstone, in a region of predominantly poorly consolidated sedimentary rocks.

CAMBRIAN

(about 590 to 515 million years ago; *Cambria* was the Roman name for Wales, the type area)

Fossils

The Cambrian sediments contain the earliest recognised invertebrates with hard parts. Trilobites (used for time-correlation of rocks in different areas) and brachiopods are important. Trilobites found in north-west Scotland differ markedly from those found in the English and Welsh outcrops. This suggests that these areas were separated by a physical feature which prevented migration of the trilobites; this barrier could have been an ocean (see below).

Areas of outcrop of special interest

North-west Scotland

Data: The sequence is several hundred metres thick, and contains marine fossils; it is unconformable on Precambrian rocks. Sandstones pass up into **dolomites** (carbonate of calcium and magnesium) and limestones.

Interpretation: The rocks were deposited in a shallow sea covering a relatively stable platform that may have been a varying distance from a land with relief that decreased through time.

Highlands of Scotland

Data: There are several thousand metres of much deformed and metamorphosed sedimentary rocks that contain marine fossils in a few places. The sequence includes muddy sandstones and mudstones. There are several thousand metres of basaltic igneous rocks in the south-west.

Interpretation. These rocks were deposited on a subsiding sea floor, with volcanic activity in places.

North Wales

Data: There are several thousand metres of deformed muddy sandstones and mudstones containing marine fossils.

Interpretation: These rocks were deposited on a subsiding sea floor.

North and west Ireland

Data: There are at least several hundred metres of much deformed and metamorphosed sedimentary rocks that contain some marine fossils. The sequence includes muddy sandstones and mudstones.

Interpretation: These rocks were deposited on a subsiding sea floor.

Midlands of England and Welsh borders

Data: There are a few hundred metres of sandstones, mudstones and limestones, containing marine fossils. Cambrian rocks are found in boreholes in the Midlands.

Interpretation: The rocks were deposited in a shallow sea covering a stable platform.

England (East Anglia)

Data: There are no outcrops of lower Palaeozoic rocks in this area, but results

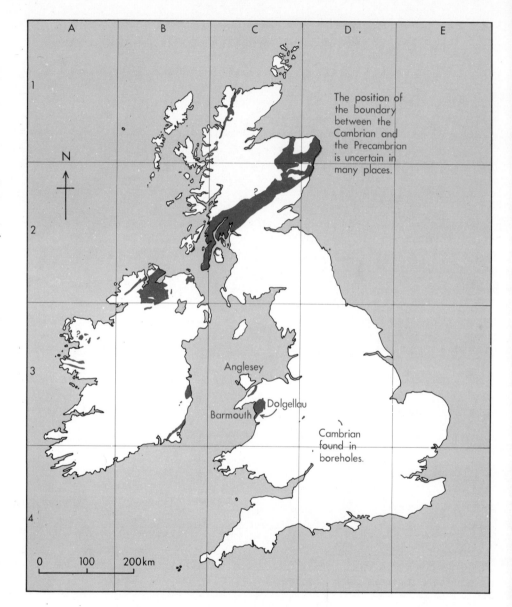

The position of the boundary between the Cambrian and the Precambrian is uncertain in many places.

Anglesey

Dolgellau
Barmouth

Cambrian found in boreholes.

0   100   200km

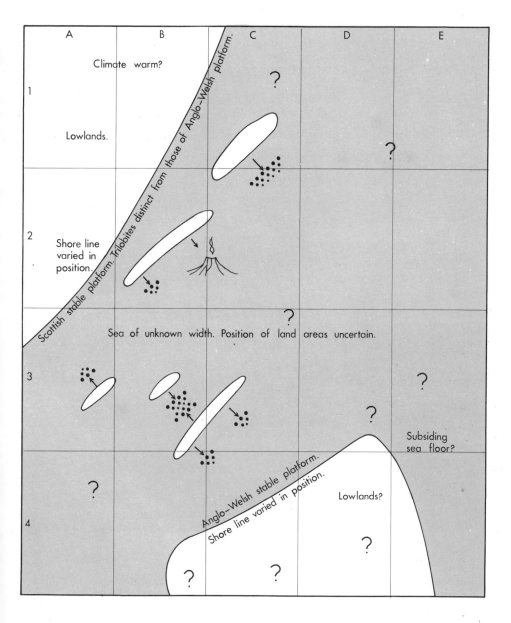

from boreholes and geophysical work indicate that beneath a thin cover of later rocks there are several thousand metres of deformed rocks of Cambrian to Silurian age.

Interpretation: Until more is known about the age and type of these rocks interpretation must remain uncertain, but it appears that this was an area where rocks were deposited on a subsiding sea floor.

Palaeogeography

A sea occupied the area between the Welsh Borders and north-west Scotland. This sea included some island source areas (for example the area of present-day Anglesey), the erosion of which supplied large amounts of mud and sand to the surrounding subsiding sea floor. North-west Scotland and the Welsh Borders were stable platforms on opposing edges of this sea; they were covered by shallow water and received relatively little sediment, mostly pure (not muddy) sandstones and limestones. The two stable platforms were farther apart than they are now, but the width of the sea between them is uncertain.

Continental drift and plate tectonics

The platforms on either side of the sea were tectonically stable and hence probably not associated with plate margins. The Scottish platform appears to have been part of a continent; the Anglo–Welsh platform may have been part of a much smaller land-mass. The width of the sea is uncertain because palaeomagnetic methods cannot determine palaeolongitudes; the distance between the separate parts of the British Isles shown on p. 9 for the Cambrian–Lower Ordovician is therefore speculative. Though no clear evidence has yet been identified in the British Isles for the existence of a plate margin or plate margins lying between the Scottish and Anglo–Welsh stable platforms during the Cambrian, there are some clues. The presence of the stable platforms themselves supports a partial analogy with the present-day Atlantic Ocean; it has been suggested that the basaltic volcanics in the south-west Highlands of Scotland indicate the incipient opening of such an ocean early in the Cambrian.

Economic

Slate quarrying in north Wales, important in the past, is now in decline. The slates were formed by post-Cambrian deformation of mudstones. The copper and gold in Cambrian rocks near Dolgellau in north Wales were emplaced by post-Cambrian mineralising fluids; the gold is found in veins, the copper is spread throughout the rocks in which it occurs. There has recently been much debate about mining these ores on a large scale; the rocks are in the Snowdonia National Park. Manganese has been mined from Cambrian mudstones in north Wales. Mudstones rich in potassium, not yet exploited, form part of the Cambrian sequence in north-west Scotland. Elsewhere the Cambrian is quarried for construction work; locally, for example at Barmouth, it has been much used as a building stone.

ORDOVICIAN

(about 515 to 445 million years ago; named after an ancient tribe in Wales, the type area)

Fossils

The graptolites are important because they were abundant, **planktonic** (free floating) and therefore widely distributed; they also evolved rapidly, which makes them excellent fossils for **zonation** (palaeontological subdivision of a sequence to aid time-correlation of rocks in different areas). There were also abundant and varied trilobites and brachiopods. The marked difference between the non-planktonic **shelly** fossils (such as brachiopods and trilobites) in north-western and south-eastern areas was maintained until late in the period.

Areas of outcrop of special interest

North-west Scotland

Data: Several hundred metres thickness of dolomites and limestones contains marine fossils of early Ordovician age.

Interpretation: This area was a stable platform covered by a shallow sea.

North-east Scotland

Data: Over one thousand metres thickness of deformed muddy sandstones and mudstones contains marine microfossils.

Interpretation: The rocks were deposited on a subsiding sea floor with varied relief.

Southern Uplands of Scotland

Data: There is a sequence up to several thousand metres thick of deformed muddy sandstones; a thick sequence of sandstones and conglomerates is found in places (Girvan); elsewhere the sequence consists of only a few tens of metres of graptolitic mudstones (Moffat). Volcanics are found in places, mostly low in the sequence.

Interpretation: The rocks were deposited on a subsiding sea floor with varied relief. Coarse sedimentary rocks formed in some areas at the foot of submarine slopes, while other parts, possibly submarine highs, received little sediment. There was volcanic activity, especially early in the period.

Wales

Data: There are up to several thousand metres of deformed andesitic volcanics, muddy sandstones and graptolitic mudstones. Much of this sequence is locally unconformable on Cambrian rocks, and in the north-west on Precambrian.

Interpretation: The rocks were deposited on a subsiding sea floor, with local island source areas, some of them formed of active volcanoes. The instability of the sea floor is indicated by local **unconformities** (time breaks in the succession).

North-west and south-east Ireland

Data: Several thousand metres of deformed sedimentary rocks contain marine

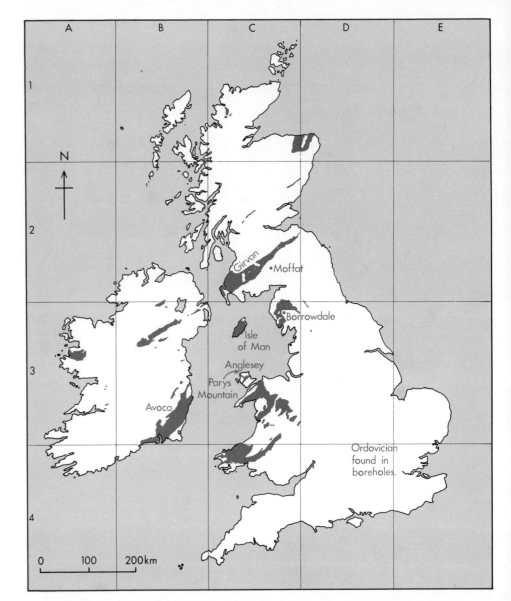

fossils. There are associated volcanic rocks which occur extensively at the top of the sequence in the south-east.

Interpretation: The rocks were deposited on a subsiding sea floor. Volcanoes were active at times, especially relatively late in the period in south-east Ireland.

Isle of Man

Data: There are several thousand metres of deformed muddy sandstones and

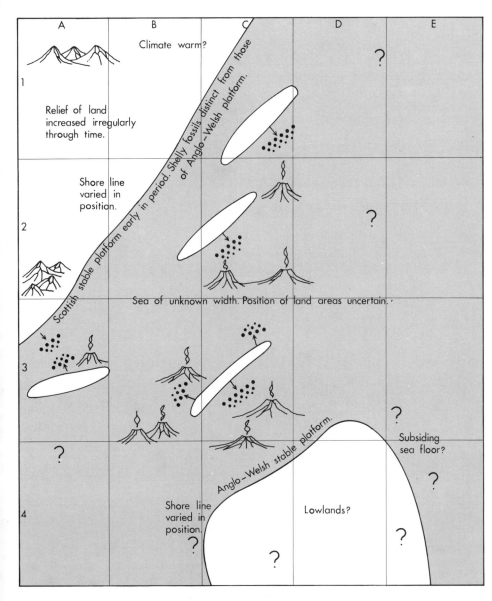

Grid labels: A B C D E (columns), 1 2 3 4 (rows)

Climate warm?

Relief of land increased irregularly through time.

Shore line varied in position.

Scottish stable platform early in period. Shelly fossils distinct from those of Anglo-Welsh platform.

Sea of unknown width. Position of land areas uncertain.

Anglo-Welsh stable platform.

Subsiding sea floor?

Shore line varied in position.

Lowlands?

graptolitic mudstones (now slates).
Interpretation: The rocks were deposited on a subsiding sea floor.

Lake District of England
Data: There are several thousand metres of deformed muddy sandstones and graptolitic mudstones (now slates); this sequence is followed by several thousand metres of andesitic volcanics.

Interpretation: There was much volcanic activity on a subsiding sea floor.

Welsh borders
Data: The sequence consists of a variable thickness (a few hundred metres or more) of mudstones passing up unconformably into a sequence, up to a few thousand metres thick in the west, of varied rocks that include **calcareous** (calcium carbonate bearing) mudstones and sandstones with shelly marine fossils. **Unconformities** (time breaks in the succession) lead to a thin sequence in places in the east.

Interpretation: In the east there was a relatively stable platform periodically covered by a shallow sea. Subsidence of the sea floor was greater and more persistent in the west.

Palaeogeography
The floor of the sea lying between the stable platforms of the Welsh Borders and north-west Scotland continued to rise and fall, and in places was covered by volcanics. Considerable subsidence is indicated by the great thicknesses of sedimentary rocks in areas like the Isle of Man and the Lake District; elsewhere, as at Moffat in the Southern Uplands of Scotland, areas received little coarse sediment. Volcanoes were active, particularly in Ireland, Wales and the Lake District. In places islands, some of volcanic origin, provided sediments to the surrounding sea floor. Relatively shallow water covered the more stable margins of the sea; on these shelf areas marine limestones formed. Fossil assemblages suggest continued quite wide separation of the Scottish and Anglo–Welsh stable platforms in the early Ordovician, followed by a removal of barriers to migration later in the period.

Continental drift and plate tectonics
Palaeomagnetic evidence places the British Isles in the southern hemisphere (while the present Sahara lay near the south pole and was subject to extensive glaciation). As noted in the Cambrian section, the extent of the separation of the north-west of the British Isles from the rest of the British Isles is uncertain. The volume and type (andesitic) of the igneous activity at this time, and the probable Ordovician age of deformation and metamorphism of some sequences in the north and west of the British Isles, suggest that the stable platform areas may have begun to move towards each other as part of the intervening ocean floor was consumed at a destructive plate margin or margins. This idea is supported by the fossil evidence discussed above.

Economic
Copper and iron ores are mined from Ordovician rocks at Avoca in south-east Ireland. Volcanic rocks of Ordovician age in north Wales are host to substantial low-grade copper deposits. A century ago Parys Mountain in Anglesey was one of the most important copper mines in the world. The main lead and zinc deposits of the Southern Uplands of Scotland are in later veins of ore cutting Ordovician rocks. The green slates of the Borrowdale Volcanics of Cumbria are a popular ornamental building material.

15

SILURIAN

(about 445 to 415 million years ago; named after an ancient tribe in Wales, the type area)

Fossils

The graptolites are the zonal fossils. Brachiopods and trilobites are a feature of the shallow water marine deposits. Corals, crinoids and bryozoans are found in abundance in some of the limestones.

Areas of outcrop of special interest

Midland Valley of Scotland

Data: The maximum total thickness of these rocks is about two thousand metres. Muddy sandstones and mudstones with marine fossils pass up into a sequence of sediments, some red, including desiccation-cracked mudstones and fish-bearing horizons.

Interpretation: The sequence indicates an upward change from a relatively deep sea to a shallow sea or non-marine environment. The red sediments may have been derived from red soils forming on land not yet bearing much plant life.

Southern Uplands of Scotland

Data: There are several thousand metres of deformed muddy sandstones and graptolitic mudstones.

Interpretation: The rocks were deposited on a subsiding sea floor.

Wales

Data: In central and northern areas there are several thousand metres of deformed muddy sandstones and graptolitic mudstones. In parts of the east and south these pass laterally into a thinner sequence of sedimentary rocks with shelly marine fossils; there is an unconformity near the base of this thinner sequence. In the south volcanics are found at the base of the sequence.

Interpretation: In central and northern areas, the rocks were deposited on a subsiding sea floor. To the east and south lay a stable platform. Early in the period there was volcanic activity in the south.

North-east Ireland

Data: Deformed muddy sandstones and mudstones form a sequence at least several hundred metres thick that includes graptolitic mudstones.

Interpretation: The rocks were deposited on a subsiding sea floor.

Lake District of England

Data: There are several thousand metres of deformed muddy sandstones and

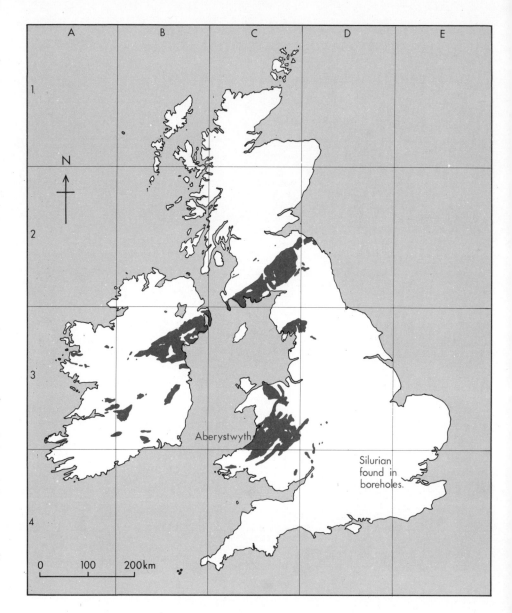

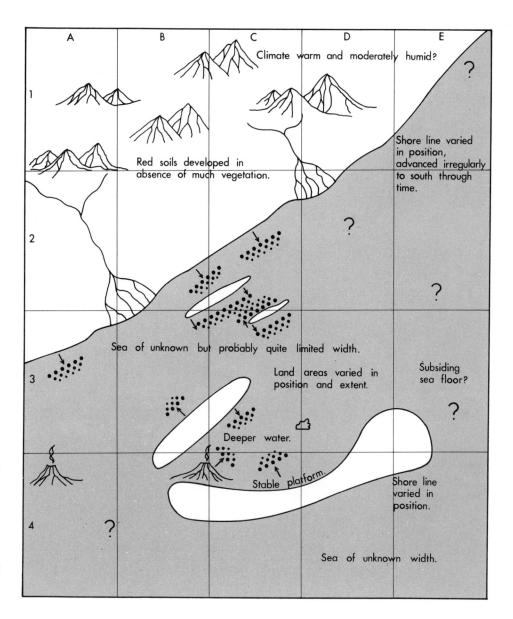

Climate warm and moderately humid?

Shore line varied in position, advanced irregularly to south through time.

Red soils developed in absence of much vegetation.

Sea of unknown but probably quite limited width.

Land areas varied in position and extent.

Subsiding sea floor?

Deeper water.

Stable platform.

Shore line varied in position.

Sea of unknown width.

mudstones containing marine fossils.
Interpretation: The rocks were deposited on a subsiding sea floor.

Welsh Borders
Data: A sequence of limestones and mudstones, about one thousand metres thick, contains shelly marine fossils and small limestone reefs which include corals.
Interpretation: These rocks were formed in a shallow sea covering a stable platform.

Palaeogeography

The sea floor continued to subside while the stable platform in the Welsh Borders persisted. The absence of Silurian rocks in northern Scotland suggests that the sea had retreated from that area, and the evidence in the Midland Valley indicates that the north-western part of the area of the British Isles formerly covered by the sea was emerging to form a relatively large area of land. Meanwhile south-eastern parts of this formerly more extensive sea continued to receive large amounts of sediment from island and other sources. A shallow sea covered the stable platform in the Welsh Borders for much of the period. There was much less volcanic activity than in the Ordovician.

Continental drift and plate tectonics

The relatively short Silurian period follows the andesitic igneous activity of the Ordovician and includes the beginning of mountain building continued in the Devonian. Taken with the disappearance of the stable platform in north-west Scotland, this suggests a continuation of the convergence of the former Scottish and the Anglo–Welsh stable platforms first indicated in the Ordovician. The intervening sea floor would in this case still have been consumed at a destructive margin or margins, though in the British Isles there is only isolated igneous activity that might be taken as evidence for this. The corals and associated algae in the reefs in the Welsh Borders provide good evidence of warm shallow seas, and support the suggestion from palaeomagnetic evidence that the British Isles were at this time in tropical or sub-tropical latitudes south of the equator.

Economic

Secondary copper, nickel and other minerals are found in Silurian rocks in the Southern Uplands of Scotland. Ores of lead and other metals are found in Silurian rocks in central Wales. Limestone is mined in the Welsh Borders. Locally, as for example at Aberystwyth, the Silurian rocks have provided building material.

DEVONIAN

(about 415 to 370 million years ago; named after Devon. The non-marine sedimentary rocks are often known familiarly as the 'Old Red Sandstone')

Fossils

Many fish are found in rocks believed to have been laid down in fresh water. Of the marine faunas, the goniatites are most important for zonation. Corals and brachiopods are common in places. Plants became established on land.

Areas of outcrop of special interest

North-east Scotland, Orkney and Shetland Islands

Data: The sequence is several thousand metres thick and consists of sandstones and mudstones with conglomerates at the base. These rocks unconformably overlie deformed earlier rocks. They contain abundant fish in places.

Interpretation: The sediments were deposited partly in lakes between mountain ranges and partly by rivers draining these mountains.

Midland Valley of Scotland

Data: There are several thousand metres of red sandstones, conglomerates and volcanics. The sedimentary rocks include fish remains.

Interpretation: The coarse beds represent river deposits formed on and near mountain fronts. There were also some intermontane lakes and contemporary volcanoes and lava flows.

South Wales and Welsh Borders

Data: There is a sequence up to a few thousand metres thick of sandstones, conglomerates and mudstones, with distinctive calcareous beds in places. The rocks contain vertebrate fossils.

Interpretation: These are in part the deposits of rivers draining a large land area. The type of calcareous bed developed indicates soils that formed in a warm, semi-arid climate with seasonal rainfall.

South-west Ireland

Data: A sequence several thousand metres thick of sandstones and mudstones, some red, includes channels filled with sandstones that are cut into the mudstones. Some mudstones are cracked by desiccation.

Interpretation: These rocks are in part the coastal plain (?) deposits of rivers draining a large land area.

South-west England

Data: Parts of a southern sequence of several thousand (?) metres thickness of deformed muddy sandstones and mudstones with marine fossils alternate in north Devon with parts of a northern sequence of a few thousand metres thickness of sedimentary rocks bearing fossil fish. Limestone reefs and volcanics are found in the south.

Interpretation: A sea of variable depth in the south, in which there was periodic

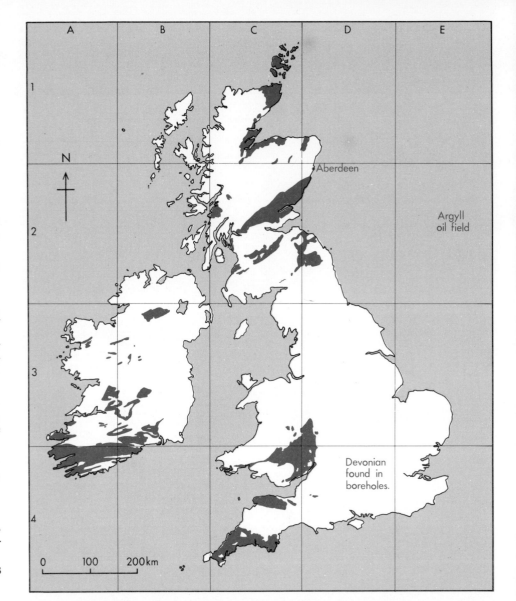

volcanic activity, was separated from land to the north by a shore line which varied in position through time.

North Sea and south and east England

Data: Devonian marine fossils are found in several boreholes in central, east and south-east England, and below the reservoirs of the Argyll oil field.

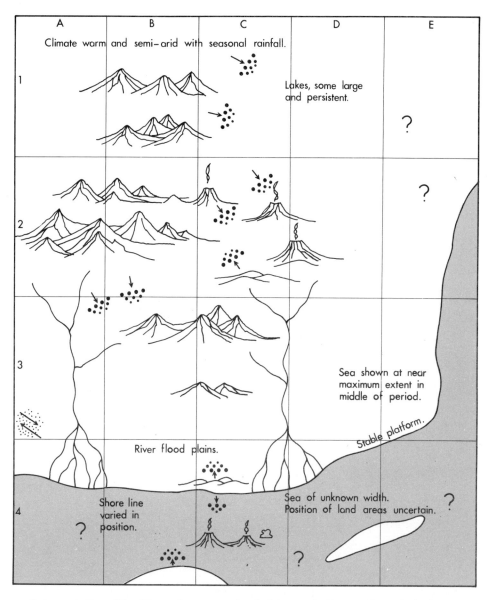

A B C D E

1   Climate warm and semi–arid with seasonal rainfall.

Lakes, some large and persistent.

?

2

?

3

Sea shown at near maximum extent in middle of period.

Stable platform.

River flood plains.

4   Shore line varied in position.

?

Sea of unknown width. Position of land areas uncertain. ?

?

Interpretation: The Devonian sea extended towards the north-east during at least part of the period.

Highlands and Southern Uplands of Scotland and Lake District of England

Data: Granites, for which a Devonian date of cooling is indicated by measurements of products of radioactive decay in several minerals (radiometric dating),

are found emplaced in deformed lower Palaeozoic rocks.

Interpretation: Granites were intruded into the deformed rocks forming the root of a mountain chain after most of the deformation by **folding** (buckling) and **faulting** (fracturing) had been completed.

Palaeogeography

The Devonian sediments indicate a drastic change in the geography of the area of the British Isles from lower Palaeozoic (Cambrian, Ordovician and Silurian) times. The central marine area became land as the former stable platform areas of north-west Scotland and the Welsh Borders completed the movement towards each other that began in the lower Palaeozoic. This movement squeezed and shortened the sedimentary and volcanic rocks between them, thereby creating **fold mountains**, which were intruded with granites. These events are referred to as the **Caledonian Orogeny**. (For some of the features of this orogeny see p. 39.) Faulting within the mountains created valleys, sometimes filled with lakes, into which was poured sediment produced by the erosion of the highlands. The redness of many of the sedimentary rocks indicates an oxidising environment of deposition and consolidation; this suggests, but does not prove, deposition on land. Meanwhile, a sea lay to the south, the evidence for which can now be seen along a belt running through southern Ireland, south-west and central England into the North Sea and central Europe. Both here and to the north, in the mountains, there was volcanic activity.

Continental drift and plate tectonics

By now the British Isles were, except possibly for parts of the south-west, more or less in one piece in tropical latitudes in the southern hemisphere. The palaeomagnetic evidence for the final convergence of the former stable platform areas tallies well with the evidence, summarised above, that sediments deposited on the floor of an intervening sea were compressed and uplifted to form mountains. This could have been a Himalayan-type orogeny caused by the collision of two continents above a destructive (granite-forming?) plate margin or margins, though there is no clear evidence that the former stable platform in the Welsh Borders was part of a land-mass of any great size. It is not known how much conservative plate motion took place during this orogeny; in other words, the north-west areas may not have approached the rest of the British Isles at right angles to the line along which they eventually joined. Clear evidence about the plate tectonics in the south has yet to be identified (see the Upper Carboniferous section).

Economic

The Devonian rocks provide local building stones (the granite of Aberdeen is a notable example) and aggregates for construction. The limestones of south-west England have been of more than local significance as **dimension stone** (quarried or cut in accordance with required dimensions). Some uranium-bearing sedimentary rocks have been identified in north-east Scotland. Post-Devonian mineralisation in south-west England (see Upper Carboniferous section) created important economic deposits of tin, tungsten and other metals in Devonian rocks, some of which are still worked.

LOWER CARBONIFEROUS

(about 370 to 325 million years ago; the name means 'coal-bearing', mainly with reference to the Upper Carboniferous)

Fossils

Goniatites are used for zonation in the mudstones, and are important in south-west England. Brachiopods and corals are used for zonation in the limestones. Amphibians are found in Scotland.

Areas of outcrop of special interest

Midland Valley of Scotland

Data: A few thousand metres thickness of sandstones and mudstones includes oil-bearing mudstones and some limestones. A thickness of over one thousand metres of lavas is found in places in the west; volcanics are also found in the east.

Interpretation: The conditions were mainly non-marine with some marine incursions. The area was one of considerable subsidence and received abundant sediment that was supplied periodically from surrounding highlands. There was much igneous activity in places.

South Wales and south-west England

Data: Several hundred metres of limestones and calcareous mudstones in the south Wales and Avon areas pass southwards in Devon and Cornwall into a deformed sequence, a few hundred metres thick, of goniatite-bearing mudstones with associated volcanics.

Interpretation: A shallow sea in the north bordered a deeper marine area to the south that received limited supplies of coarse sediment, and in which there was some volcanic activity.

Ireland

Data: Several hundred metres thickness of widespread limestones, including reef limestones, calcareous mudstones and local volcanics, in central and southern areas, passes into a few thousand metres thickness of sandstones and mudstones to the north.

Interpretation: An extensive shallow sea, in which there was some volcanic activity, was bordered by a highland source area in the north.

North England

Data: The sequence is well over one thousand metres thick in places. Sandstones and mudstones, with some limestones and thin coals, pass to the south into limestones, which include reefs, and calcareous mudstones.

Interpretation: A shallow sea in the south was bordered by a land in the north that supplied sand and mud to near-shore areas.

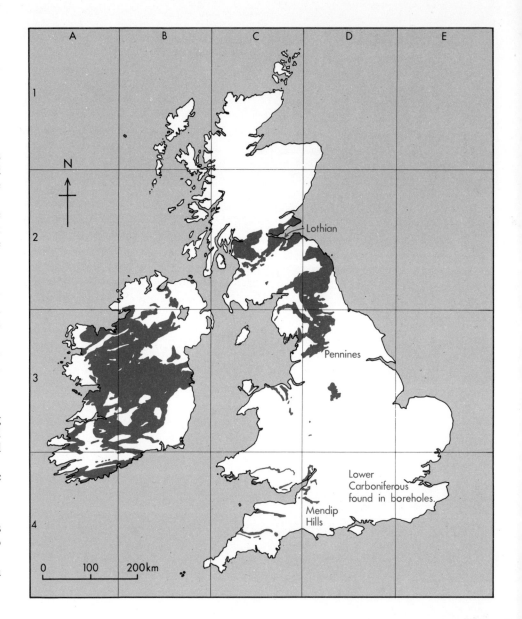

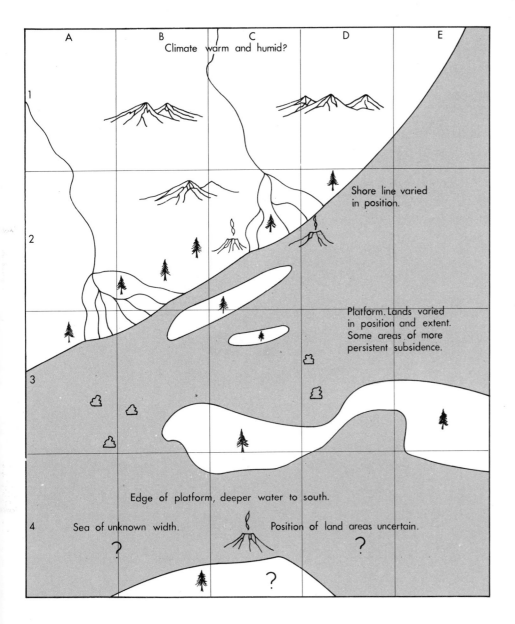

Climate warm and humid?

Shore line varied in position.

Platform. Lands varied in position and extent. Some areas of more persistent subsidence.

Edge of platform, deeper water to south.

Sea of unknown width.

Position of land areas uncertain.

Palaeogeography

Most of the area of the British Isles, except the north, was gradually invaded by a shallow sea in which limestones developed, especially in the south away from sources of **terrigenous** ('land-formed', non-carbonate) sediment. The mountains in the north formed in the Caledonian orogeny continued to supply much sediment to northern areas, but the material was mainly much less coarse than that produced during the Devonian. In parts of this northern area there was substantial volcanic activity. In places in the shallow sea to the south reefs were formed. Meanwhile in the far south the deeper sea established by Devonian times persisted.

Continental drift and plate tectonics

The only area in which there appears to have been an active plate margin or margins is in the south, and, as indicated in the Devonian section, the evidence is still unclear. Some of the data bearing on this problem are considered in the Upper Carboniferous section. It has been suggested, not without opposition, that some of the mineralisation of the Carboniferous noted below was associated with the formation of large fractures, which were in turn related to the earliest stages of splitting of the recently formed land-mass along a constructive plate margin. It should be noted that attempts to relate economic deposits to plate tectonics are at an early and hence rather speculative stage. That is not to say that they are not worthwhile (see the Jurassic section). The abundant limestones support the palaeomagnetic evidence that places the area of the British Isles in low latitudes during the Lower Carboniferous.

Economic

The widespread limestones are important in the chemical and other industries and for cement making; they are crushed for use as aggregates in the construction industry, and are used as dimension stone. In Ireland, the Pennines, north Wales and the Mendip Hills, limestones are host rocks to later deposits of minerals containing (in places) lead, zinc, silver, copper, mercury, fluorine and barium; the Irish deposits are specially important. In south Wales and Cumbria later hematite iron ore deposits are found in the limestones. Oil-bearing mudstones were mined in Lothian until recently.

UPPER CARBONIFEROUS
(about 325 to 280 million years ago)

Fossils
Goniatites are used for zonation in south-west England. Bivalves and plants are useful for zoning non-marine sediments. Large trees flourished.

Areas of outcrop of special interest

Midland Valley of Scotland
Data: There are up to a few thousand metres of sandstones, mudstones and coals, with limestones in the lower part of the sequence. There are some volcanics.
Interpretation: Marine influence diminished through time as widespread coal swamps formed in river deltas and flood plains flanking the persistent northern land-mass. Volcanic activity continued from the Lower Carboniferous, but on a reduced scale.

South Wales and the North and Midlands of England
Data: Total thicknesses are up to several thousand metres. Sandstones and mudstones with some goniatites, pass up into a repetitive sequence of mud-stones, sandstones, coal seams, and in some cases beds with marine fossils.
Interpretation: There is a change through time from partly marine conditions to predominantly non-marine coal swamps where the repetitive sequences probably indicate periodic changes in the position of the delta distributary channels. From time to time there was a temporary but widespread advance of the sea over the coal swamps. There was a plentiful supply of sediment for much of the time.

South-west England
Data: A deformed sequence of muddy sandstones and mudstones, well over one thousand metres thick, contains goniatites that are rare in the upper part of the sequence. Varied sedimentary rocks are found in the north of the area; these include sandstones filling channels cut into mudstones. Large granites, for example Dartmoor, cut previously deformed Carboniferous and Devonian rocks. Radiometric dating indicates late Carboniferous to early Permian cooling of these granites.
Interpretation: The rocks were deposited on a subsiding sea floor with varied relief. To the north lay shallower marine and fluvial environments. The area as a whole became less persistently marine through time. The whole sequence was finally deformed, and intruded by granite magmas.

Palaeogeography
Partly because of the great economic importance of the coal that gives it its name, the Upper Carboniferous palaeogeography is known in some detail. The northern highlands continued to supply sediment, which spread south-

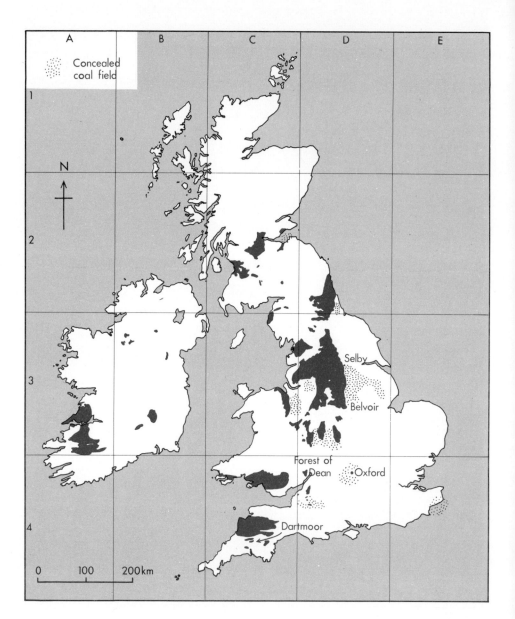

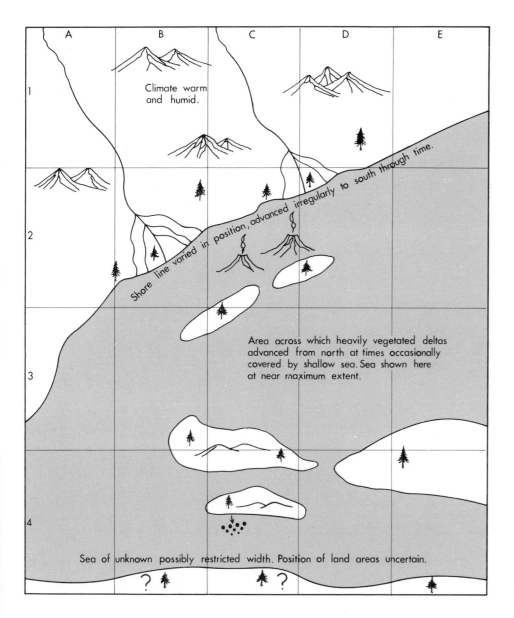

Climate warm and humid.

Shore line varied in position, advanced irregularly to south through time.

Area across which heavily vegetated deltas advanced from north at times occasionally covered by shallow sea. Sea shown here at near maximum extent.

Sea of unknown possibly restricted width. Position of land areas uncertain.

wards over the limestones formed during the Lower Carboniferous. Large deltas formed, and on these coal swamps developed. Apart from occasional advances, the sea retreated to the far south of the area of the British Isles, where a relatively deep sea received large amounts of sediment. Later in the Carboniferous this sea showed signs of becoming shallower.

Continental drift and plate tectonics

The palaeomagnetic evidence that the British Isles were in equatorial latitudes in the Carboniferous fits well with the independent evidence of a warm humid climate provided by the great quantities of fossil plant material preserved in the extensive coal deposits, and by the **leached** (chemically altered by much weathering) soils preserved in parts of the coal measure sequence. These deposits are not only found under the North Sea and across Europe, but also in North America, which was then much nearer to the British Isles (see the Devonian and Tertiary sections). The evidence in the south for shallowing of the sea may be interpreted in several ways in terms of plate tectonics. There is general agreement that a destructive plate margin or margins, present from at least the Devonian onwards, finally caused the late Carboniferous – early Permian mountain building. Whether this was the result of a simple collision of continents is doubtful. It has been suggested that some of the extensive rises and falls in Upper Carboniferous sea level, associated with the repetitive marine–freshwater sequences, may have been caused by variations in the size of the ice sheet then covering a former large southern continent lying in high latitudes.

Economic

There are important coal fields in Scotland, Wales, and north and central England. Recent boreholes have revealed extensive concealed coal deposits in the Selby area east of the Pennines, beneath the Vale of Belvoir in the east Midlands of England, and near Oxford. Upper Carboniferous coals beneath the southern North Sea are the likely source of the gas in the overlying Permian sandstones. Upper Carboniferous sandstones have proved good building stones in many regions, and in the Pennines a former use of the sandstones gave the name Millstone Grit to the lower part of the sequence. The possible use of old quarries as tips provides problems of conservation. Some mudstones, formed from leached Carboniferous soils, are exploited for the manufacture of refractory bricks. Important mineralisation, especially with tin ores, was associated with the intrusion of the granites in south-west England. Tin mining has recently been restarted. Later alteration of parts of the granite formed extensive deposits of **kaolinite** (china clay) on which an important open-pit mining industry is based. The impact of this industry on the landscape has been the subject of much debate.

PERMIAN

(about 280 to 240 million years ago; named after Perm in the U.S.S.R.)

Fossils

These are not abundant in most of the Permian rocks of the British Isles, which leads to such difficulty in separating the Permian and Triassic rocks in many areas that they are commonly discussed together (as the 'New Red Sandstone', compared to the 'Old Red Sandstone' of the Devonian), even though the Permian marks, on the sound evidence of the affinities of its fossils, the end of the Palaeozoic era. Traces of reptilian footprints are found in places. Spores of plants are useful zonal fossils; microfossil studies have been given a fillip in the British Isles by the offshore exploration for oil and gas, because microfossils are much more abundant and better preserved than are larger fossils in many rock chips from drilling.

Areas of outcrop of special interest

South-west Scotland and Isle of Arran

Data: The sequence is up to several hundred metres thick in places; the thickness varies considerably over short distances. The sequence consists of red sandstones with interbedded conglomerates. The sandstone bodies contain many well rounded grains and show large scale **cross-bedding** (internal planes at an angle to the main bedding planes, the latter indicating the original, nearly horizontal plane on which the whole bed was formed).

Interpretation: This was a desert occupied by a field of sand dunes. The most commonly found slope of the cross-bedding, which is to the west, indicates that the prevailing wind came from the east. Conglomerates were washed in from surrounding highlands during occasional storms, and formed alluvial fans. Considerable changes in the thickness of the sequence over short distances indicate that deposition of the thicker sequences took place in valleys separated from the adjacent highlands by faults.

North-east England

Data: The total thickness is a few hundred metres. Sandstone bodies, containing many well rounded grains, and with large scale cross-bedding, pass up first into limestones and then into **evaporites** (rocks containing minerals formed by the desiccation of sea water in a characteristic sequence controlled by relative solubility: gypsum (relatively insoluble) to **halite** (common salt) to potassium salts (relatively soluble)).

Interpretation: First a sandy shoreline was covered by the advance of a warm, shallow sea in which limestone reefs were able to grow. Then, as the sea dried up (several times), the various salts came out of solution in sequence. At times desiccation was so complete that even potassium salts were precipitated in a sea by now much reduced in volume and extent (note the extent of potassium salts compared with halite shown on the outcrop map). A smaller sea developed farther west. The depth of such seas is debated; some geologists believe that

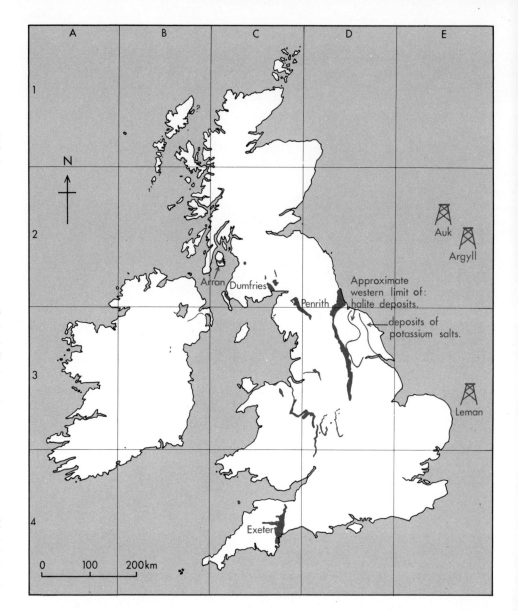

many evaporites are formed in shallow marine lagoons or on land in salt lakes and flats, and they point to the present-day Persian Gulf for examples of some of these processes. The Permian evaporites of the British Isles undoubtedly represent a range of environments.

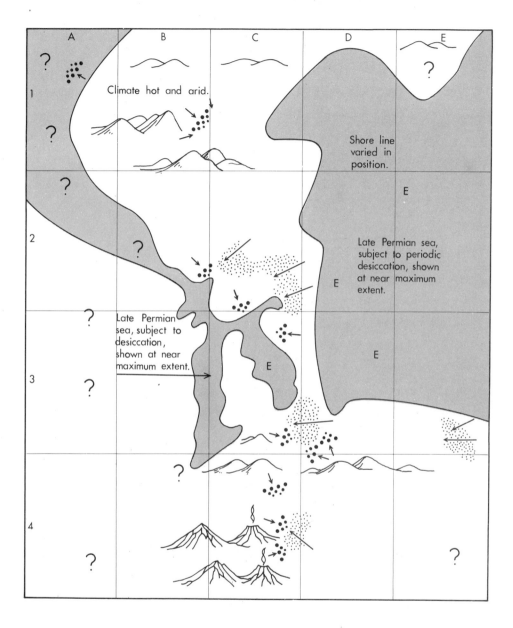

possibly farther south in the area of the present English Channel.
Interpretation: Following uplift and erosion of the earlier rocks, some areas of alluvial fan deposition within the highlands became established. These received sediments eroded from the highlands themselves and were the sites of several lava flows. Wind-formed sand dunes developed in places.

Southern North Sea
Data: (For a brief discussion of the nature of offshore data see p. 38.) Total thickness is up to several hundred metres. Red sandstones, containing many well rounded grains, and with large scale cross-bedding, pass up into evaporites.
Interpretation: Desert dune fields, in which the prevailing wind was from east to west, were flooded by seas from which salts were deposited following desiccation.

Palaeogeography
The Permian, like the Devonian, marked a drastic change in the palaeogeography of the British Isles. The undeformed Permian rocks of south-west England overlie the roots of mountains formed in the **Hercynian Orogeny** at the close of the Carboniferous and in the early Permian. Much of the British Isles was land during the Permian; only in northern England did seas persist for any great time and they were subject to the periodic desiccation to which the evaporites bear witness. Over the rest of the land fields of sand dunes formed in the prevailing east winds; the dunes were flanked in places by coarser material brought down from surrounding highlands in sudden floods.

Continental drift and plate tectonics
The evidence of prevailing east winds noted above supports the indications from palaeomagnetic work that the British Isles, with a polar orientation close to that at present, were now in tropical, trade wind latitudes in the northern hemisphere. The evidence from the evaporite deposits of a hot, arid climate also agrees with this picture. The formation of the mountains at the beginning of the period in the south has been discussed in the Upper Carboniferous section. By now the British Isles had become a stable part of a plate, though both onshore and offshore volcanic activity is believed by some geologists to mark the early stages of the splitting of the continental mass formed during the Caledonian and Hercynian orogenies.

Economic
The evaporites in north-east England formed the original basis for the large chemical industry of the region. They supply gypsum and halite (ordinary salt), as well as the rarer (more soluble) potassium salts. The potassium is used mainly for fertilizer. The sandstones formed in desert dunes tend to be very porous and permeable, and hence form good aquifers. They form excellent reservoirs for gas in the southern North Sea, where the impermeable overlying evaporites form a good cap rock to seal in the gas. Locally, for example at Dumfries and Penrith, they provide a good building stone. The possible use of aquifers as storage places for gas provides problems of conservation.

South-west England
Data: A few hundred metres thickness of red conglomerates and sandstones, some of the sandstones containing many well rounded grains and showing large scale cross-bedding, overlies unconformably the deformed and intruded Devonian and Carboniferous rocks. There are volcanics near Exeter and

25

TRIASSIC

(about 240 to 200 million years ago; the name comes from the three-fold division of Triassic rocks in Germany)

Fossils

The general comments in the Permian section apply. Spores of plants are useful zonal fossils.

Areas of outcrop of special interest

Isle of Arran, Scotland

Data: A few hundred metres thickness of sandstones and mudstones, the latter cracked by desiccation in places, contains some traces of near-shore (?) invertebrate fossils, and some limestones. In its uppermost part the sequence contains a few marine fossils.

Interpretation: The Permian desert was succeeded by a more persistently subaqueous environment, which in turn was at least partly covered by the sea at the end of the period.

North-east Scotland

Data: A sequence over one hundred metres thick of sandstones with some conglomerates includes large scale cross-bedded sandstones containing many well rounded grains. Reptilian remains and tracks are found.

Interpretation: This was a desert with sand dunes and some animal life.

North-east Ireland

Data: A sequence several hundred metres thick of mudstones and sandstones, some red, includes beds of evaporites.

Interpretation: The area, land for most of the period, was at times covered by seas that evaporated and produced salt deposits. An alternative interpretation of the origin of many evaporites is that they are formed in shallow marine lagoons, or inland in salt lakes and flats. The shores of the Persian Gulf provide modern examples of some of these processes. The Triassic evaporites of the British Isles undoubtedly represent a range of environments.

Midlands of England

Data: The total thickness is well over one thousand metres in places. Conglomerates and sandstones, including some sandstones containing many well rounded grains and forming large scale cross-bedding, pass up into red mudstones with evaporites; the evaporites are especially well developed in Cheshire. Rocks with marine fossils form the top of the sequence.

Interpretation: These lowland areas, at times covered by a field of sand dunes, received less coarse sediment through time; they were periodically covered by temporary seas, or large inland salt lakes, which evaporated to produce thick salt deposits in places. More normal marine conditions were established by the end of the period.

South-west England

Data: Maximum thicknesses are several hundred metres. Conglomerates and

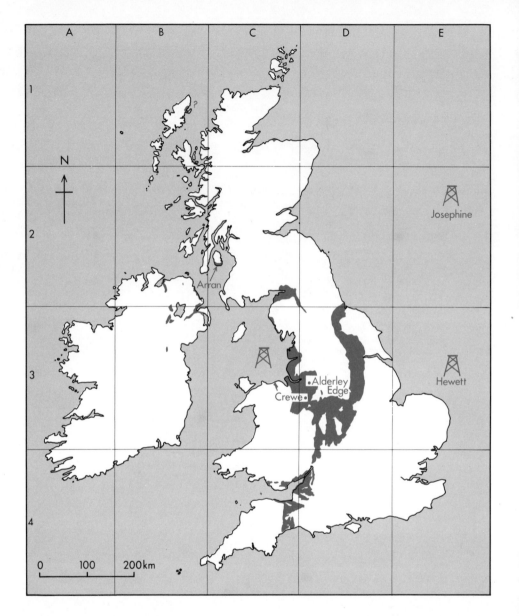

sandstones with red mudstones and evaporites pass up into thin mudstones and limestones with a limited range of marine fossils.

Interpretation: A landscape with some relief, in parts of which coarse sediment was deposited near highlands, was flattened by continuing erosion and deposition

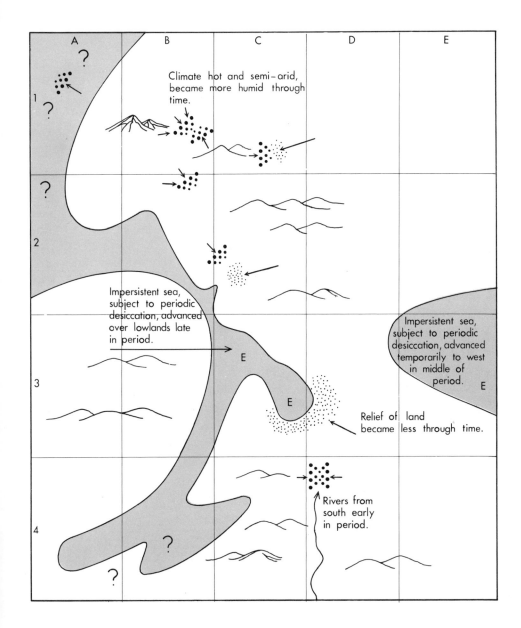

Climate hot and semi-arid, became more humid through time.

Impersistent sea, subject to periodic desiccation, advanced over lowlands late in period.

Impersistent sea, subject to periodic desiccation, advanced temporarily to west in middle of period.

Relief of land became less through time.

Rivers from south early in period.

and finally was covered by the sea.

North Sea

Data: The total thickness is well over one thousand metres in places. There is much lateral variation in thickness. Red mudstones and coarser sedimentary rocks pass up into a repetitive sequence of evaporites, mudstones and limestones. *Interpretation:* A landscape with some relief gave way to a flat lowland periodically covered by impermanent seas from the desiccation of which evaporites were formed. The large lateral changes in thickness indicate control of deposition by contemporaneous faulting.

Palaeogeography

During the Triassic there was a gradual change in the area of the British Isles from a semi-arid land, with considerable relief in places, to a more humid low-lying area, partly flooded in the middle and at the end of the period by a shallow sea. The mountains formed in the Hercynian orogeny in the south became progressively less important, both as a source of sediment and as a barrier to any advance of the sea. Local highlands elsewhere were worn down and eventually buried in the thick deposits of fine-grained sediment. Flat plains like those of the present-day Persian Gulf area lay between the higher areas. When areas such as Cheshire were covered by the sea or large salt lakes, it was for a relatively short time; the thickness of the salt deposits indicates that a great quantity of water was evaporated. Only at the very end of the period did the sea cover much of the area of the British Isles, establishing a new pattern of palaeogeography which was to last for much of the rest of the Mesozoic.

Continental drift and plate tectonics

As in the Permian, the palaeomagnetic evidence of a tropical latitude tallies with the independent evidence of a hot, semi-arid climate. The area of the British Isles was now relatively stable tectonically and apparently no longer near plate margins. Some of the faulting that controlled sedimentation may have been associated with more active plate tectonics elsewhere, such as the beginnings of the separation of major continental areas farther south-west at a constructive margin, movements which led to the formation of the early Atlantic Ocean.

Economic

The sandstones have been much used as aquifers and as building stone, and poorly consolidated conglomerates are quarried as a source of gravel. The Cheshire salt (halite) is mined for treating icy roads and has been exploited for other uses in the chemical and food industries by solution mining. Former ill-considered pumping of salt-saturated groundwater led to extensive subsidence; travellers by rail are aware of this as they cross slowly a partly flooded plain just north of Crewe. Salt is still exploited by controlled pumping in the north and west Midlands of England; gypsum is mined farther east. Some gas is produced from Triassic sandstones in the southern North Sea, where evaporites help to form good cap rocks above permeable sandstones. Secondary copper deposits in conglomerates and sandstones at Alderley Edge in Cheshire were formerly mined.

JURASSIC

(about 200 to 135 million years ago; named after the Jura Mountains of Switzerland)

Fossils

Important marine fossils are ammonites (used for zonation), bivalves, belemnites, corals and brachiopods. Land animals included reptiles such as dinosaurs.

Areas of outcrop of special interest

Scotland (scattered outcrops)

Data: This is a sequence, up to several hundred metres thick, of sandstones, mudstones and limestones with ammonites. Other rocks contain brackish-water and freshwater fossils.

Interpretation: These rocks were deposited in, or on the edge of, a relatively shallow sea of variable depth and extent.

England (belt from north-east to south coast)

Data: There is a variable thickness (maximum well over one thousand metres) of limestones and mudstones with ammonites. There are some coral beds. Sandstones and coals are found in places in the north-east. Evaporites, non-marine fossils and fossil soils are found at the top of the sequence in the south; only in the south is there a continuous sequence up into the Cretaceous.

Interpretation: There was a shallow, warm sea in which limestones were deposited and into which large amounts of mud were introduced from time to time. Local areas of sea floor with higher relief received less sediment. Areas in the north were apparently at times near to a quite large land source of sediment and carbonaceous material. The disappearance of ammonites from much of southern England towards the end of the Jurassic marks the introduction of brackish- to freshwater conditions following withdrawal and desiccation of the sea.

North Sea

Data: Unconformities are found within this faulted sequence, which is of variable thickness, exceeding one thousand metres in places. Sandstones containing some marine fossils in the north give way to mudstones farther south. Volcanics are interbedded with the sedimentary rocks in some northern areas.

Interpretation: Contemporaneous faulting caused differential subsidence and uplift of parts of the area. Volcanic activity accompanied these movements in the north, where relatively thick sandstones, at least partly marine, formed in places. Farther south, away from the main supply of coarse sediments, some limestones formed in a shallow sea.

Sea of the Hebrides

Data: Geophysical work and limited direct sampling by cores indicate the presence of about one thousand metres of varied Jurassic sedimentary rocks containing marine fossils. These conformably overlie Permo–Triassic red beds in places and are preserved in down-faulted areas.

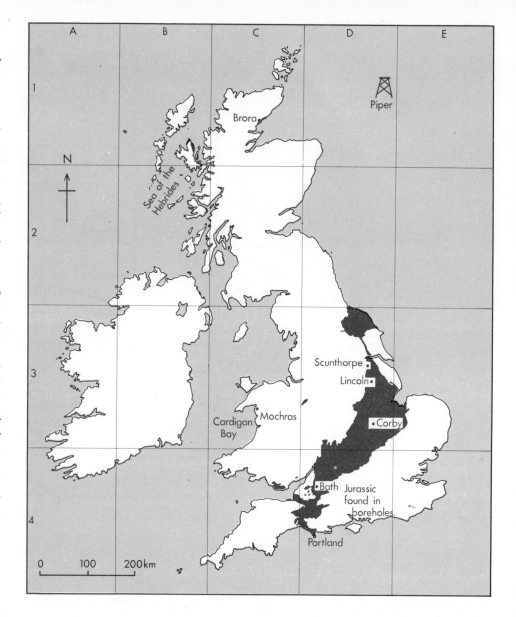

Interpretation: Flooding of Permo–Triassic land areas by a Jurassic sea led to quite substantial deposition of sediments; these sediments have been preserved by faulting that may have been at least partly contemporaneous.

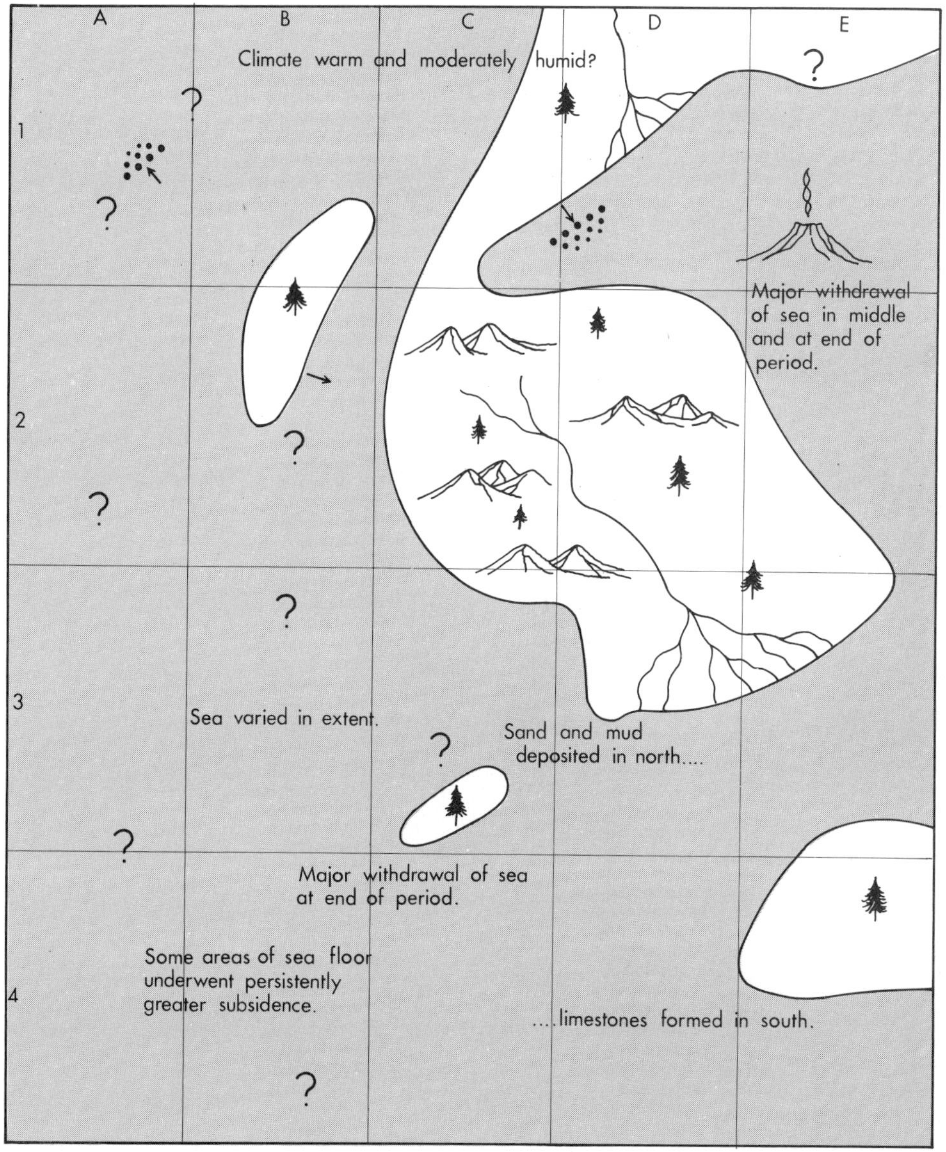
A
B
C
D
E
1
2
3
4
Climate warm and moderately humid?
Major withdrawal of sea in middle and at end of period.
Sea varied in extent.
Sand and mud deposited in north....
Major withdrawal of sea at end of period.
Some areas of sea floor underwent persistently greater subsidence.
....limestones formed in south.

North Wales and Cardigan Bay

Data: A deep borehole at Mochras near Harlech penetrated a sequence of lower Jurassic mudstones over one thousand metres thick that contains marine fossils. Boreholes and geophysical work in Cardigan Bay indicate a later Jurassic sequence of limestones, mudstones and sandstones that is over one thousand metres thick, contains some marine fossils, and is unconformable on lower Jurassic rocks.

Interpretation: In the early Jurassic substantial deposition of fine-grained sediment took place on the floor of a sea occupying at least part of the area of the present-day Irish Sea. Following a period of local uplift and erosion, more varied sediments were deposited, at least some of them on or near land.

Palaeogeography

Shallow seas spread over much of the land area worn down during the Permian and Triassic. Remaining islands and peninsulas of land supplied mainly relatively fine-grained sediment to near-by areas. The absence of major land source areas during much of the Jurassic in southern areas led to the formation of much organic calcium carbonate in the clear, warm seas. Farther north, nearer larger and more persistent land areas, limestone development was somewhat masked and hindered by a more constant supply of sand and mud from rivers. In the area of the present North Sea volcanic activity at times accompanied phases of faulting and uplift. These earth movements controlled and at times interrupted deposition; the sediments were at least partly marine. Towards the close of the Jurassic the sea retreated from much of the area of the British Isles.

Continental drift and plate tectonics

The abundant limestones and the apparently warm-water marine fauna support the palaeomagnetic evidence of a more southerly position for the British Isles than at present. The faulting that apparently controlled much of the sedimentation in the North Sea, and hence ultimately the origin and migration of oil and gas there, was accompanied by some of the igneous activity associated with the early stages in the development of a constructive plate margin. This development did not proceed in the North Sea, but farther south-west the early Atlantic Ocean began to form.

Economic

The Jurassic sandstones beneath the North Sea act as major oil reservoirs; fields such as Brent (off map) and Piper are based on discoveries in such rocks. At Brora, in north-east Scotland, Britain's northernmost coal mine has provided a minor source of fossil fuel. In southern Jurassic outcrops, limestones are important as building materials (the rock quarried at Portland and Bath being especially famous for its use in buildings in London, Bath and elsewhere) and as a basis for cement manufacture. Limestone from the Lincoln area is an important source of building stone. Ironstones in the main north-east to south-west outcrop in England still provide low-grade ore near Scunthorpe and Corby. The mudstones associated with the limestones are important for brick manufacture. Clays known as **fuller's earth**, from an earlier use as an absorber of grease in the cloth industry, are exploited in southern England for use as fillers and filters. Gypsum is mined from upper Jurassic rocks in south-east England. The exploitation of the Jurassic, which underlies some beautiful agricultural land near major centres of population, poses very difficult environmental problems.

LOWER CRETACEOUS

(about 135 to 95 million years ago; the name comes from the Latin for chalk, with reference to the Upper Cretaceous)

Fossils

Ammonites, belemnites and foraminifera are used for zoning marine beds; ostracods and plant spores are used for zoning non-marine beds.

Areas of outcrop of special interest

South-east England

Data: There is a thickness of several hundred metres of mudstones and sandstones. Some lower beds contain non-marine fossils, including vascular plants in their growth positions. Many of the non-marine sandstones fill braided channel networks cut into similar and finer-grained sediments. Sandstones and mudstones with marine fossils form the upper part of the sequence. Some of the sandstones with marine fossils contain sedimentary structures that indicate a shallow sea with strong tides.

Interpretation: Tidal seas periodically advanced and retreated over a land area subject to vertical (probably fault) movements and drained by rivers that flowed in from the west on the evidence of the composition of the coarser-grained sediments. There was an irregular advance of the sea to the west through time.

North Sea

Data: A varied sequence in the south consists of several hundred metres of sandstones, limestones and mudstones with marine fossils. Farther north a sequence of several hundred metres of mudstones and limestones containing marine fossils is flanked in places to the north and west by coarser sediments.

Interpretation: A partly marine area that bordered land in the south received some relatively coarse-grained material. Farther north mud was deposited and limestones formed in deeper water away from major sources of sediment, that is, away from the mouths of rivers draining the land to the north and west.

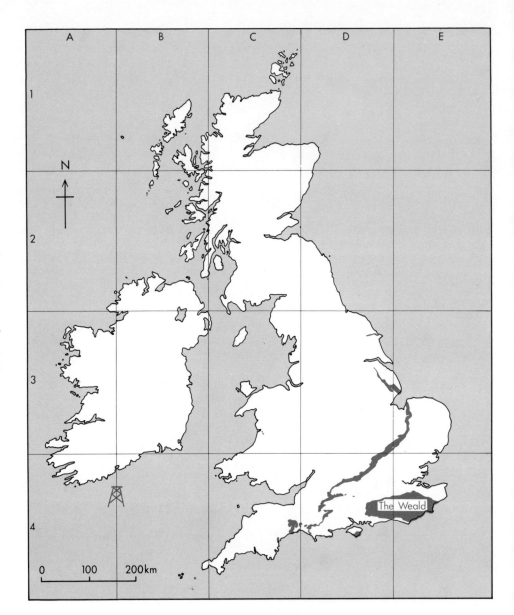

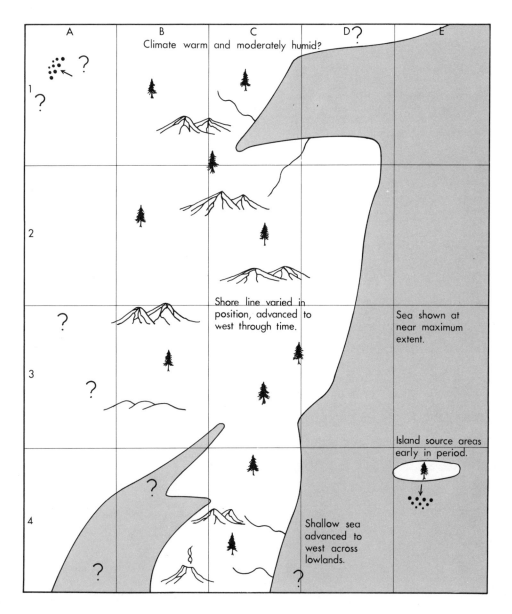

Palaeogeography

Uplift at the end of the Jurassic exposed land in the west and some small island fault-blocks elsewhere to erosion. The composition of the coarse-grained sediments in southern England indicates derivation from highlands to the west and south-west, and from uplands in the London–East Anglia area. The varied rocks in south-east England indicate relatively minor earth movements and changes in sea level; there was an irregular advance of the sea towards the west during the Lower Cretaceous. In the north land lying to the north and west supplied some coarse sediment to a sea occupying part of what is now the northern North Sea.

Continental drift and plate tectonics

The partial withdrawal of the sea at the end of the Jurassic and changes in sea level during the Lower Cretaceous may have been related to major plate movements, perhaps those associated with the opening of the North Atlantic Ocean. Like the igneous activity off south-west England, the sea level changes have been connected by some geologists with uplift that preceded the opening of part of the North Atlantic during the Upper Cretaceous. The fossil plants and other evidence indicate a warm climate; these data support palaeomagnetic evidence of a more southerly position than at present for the area of the British Isles during the Lower Cretaceous.

Economic

Fuller's earth (see Jurassic section) is exploited, and sandstones and mudstones are used for the construction industry. Sedimentary ironstones were formerly smelted in The Weald. A gas field has been discovered in sandstones off southern Ireland.

UPPER CRETACEOUS

(about 95 to 65 million years ago)

Fossils

Echinoderms, bivalves, belemnites and ammonites are used for zonation. The chalk itself is largely composed of marine microfossils (see below).

Areas of outcrop of special interest

Scotland and north and south-west Ireland (scattered outcrops)

Data: In Scotland there are sequences only a few metres thick of sandstones and **chalk** (very pure fine-grained limestone consisting mainly of tiny marine fossils). Thicker chalk is found in northern Ireland and a small patch in south-west Ireland. Carbonaceous beds that are interbedded with basaltic lavas on Mull contain plant remains that may be late Cretaceous forms.

Interpretation: These were land areas partly covered at times by a shallow sea. Major igneous activity may have begun late in the period.

South-east England

Data: There are several hundred metres of chalk.

Interpretation: The variable environments of the Lower Cretaceous were flooded by an extensive sea. In the almost total absence of any input of terrigenous sediment, the rock formed on the floor of this sea was almost pure calcium carbonate, built up largely from the very fine-grained calcareous skeletons of fossil plankton.

North Sea

Data: The sequence, over one thousand metres thick in places, is chalk in the south, which becomes muddier when traced to the north, and contains marine fossils throughout.

Interpretation: The variable Lower Cretaceous sediments in the south were blanketed by chalk. Only in the north was much non-carbonate material deposited, suggesting either relics of land in that direction or possibly a sea floor

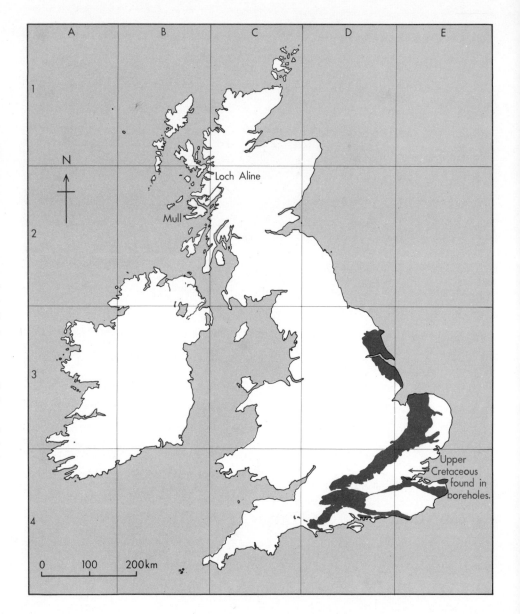

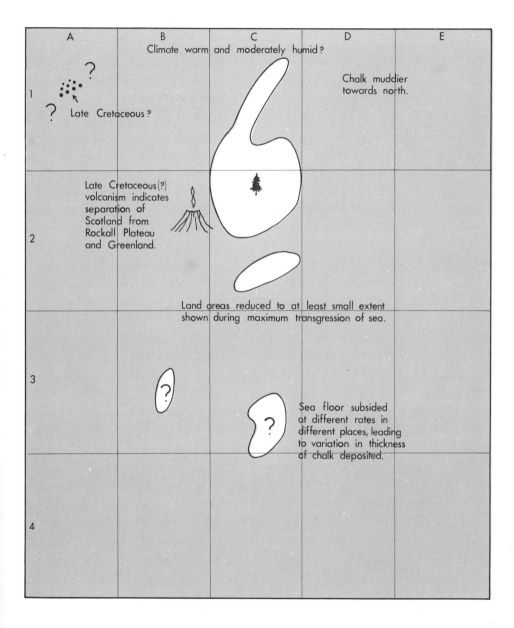

	A	B	C	D	E
1	? ? Late Cretaceous ?	Climate warm and moderately humid?		Chalk muddier towards north.	
2	Late Cretaceous (?) volcanism indicates separation of Scotland from Rockall Plateau and Greenland.				
3		Land areas reduced to at least small extent shown during maximum transgression of sea.			
4			Sea floor subsided at different rates in different places, leading to variation in thickness of chalk deposited.		

so deep that descending carbonate was dissolved before it reached the bottom, or both.

Palaeogeography

The Chalk sea advanced across the pre-existing sands and muds and over their source lands. The Chalk therefore covered a wide area of the British Isles and almost escaped admixture with terrigenous sediment. Only in the north and west is there any indication at all of near-by land. Volcanic activity may have begun in the north-west in the late Cretaceous. The **transgression** (advance) of the Chalk sea was probably the largest in the **Phanerozoic** (post-Precambrian) geological history of the British Isles.

Continental drift and plate tectonics

The widespread transgression of the Upper Cretaceous, affecting many parts of the world outside the British Isles, has been related to major uplift of ocean floors associated with the formation and rapid development of constructive plate margins. Such uplifts could have been remote from the area of the British Isles. The igneous activity associated with the formation of constructive margins between the British Isles, Greenland and North America may have begun in the north-west of the British Isles in the late Cretaceous. This part of the North Atlantic Ocean was perhaps beginning to develop. The abundant formation of calcium carbonate may indicate support for palaeomagnetic evidence of a more southerly location for the British Isles than at present.

Economic

North Sea oil fields producing from the Chalk include Dan and Ekofisk (both off map), in both of which there is also early Tertiary chalk. On land chalk is widely quarried for cement manufacture and other purposes. It is an important aquifer especially in the London area. A very pure quartz glass–sand is mined in the Upper Cretaceous at Loch Aline, west Scotland.

TERTIARY

(about 65 to 2 million years ago; named originally as the third great division of geological time)

Fossils

Foraminifera, molluscs and plant spores are used for zonation. Plants are also locally important as indicators of climate. Evolution of the mammals led to early man at the very end of the Tertiary.

Areas of outcrop of special interest

Scotland (West Coast and Islands) and North Ireland

Data: Widespread igneous rocks are found, especially **lavas** (originally molten or partly molten material extruded from volcanoes); complex volcanic centres and **dyke** (thin, vertical igneous intrusion) swarms are characteristic. The sequence of lavas is well over one thousand metres thick in places. Nine **plutonic** (deep-seated) igneous centres are known. Farther south is Lundy granite.

Interpretation: The west of Scotland formed part of an area that included the Faeroe Islands and Greenland, in which volcanic activity was widespread and periodically intense throughout much of the early Tertiary. Old volcanoes can be recognised; from these and other fissures large flows of lava poured out over the land.

South-east England

Data: Up to several hundred metres of sediments lie unconformably on the Cretaceous Chalk. Beds containing freshwater and brackish-water fossils to the north and west alternate with those containing marine forms to the south and east. The sequence represents only a part of early Tertiary time.

Interpretation: The area was land for much of Tertiary, drained by rivers supplying sediment to a sea lying to the south-east. This sea periodically advanced over the deposits of non-marine sediment forming near the shore.

North Sea

Data: The sequence contains marine fossils and is a few thousand metres thick in places. In central and northern areas limestones, sandstones and mudstones pass up into mostly fine-grained sedimentary rocks. Volcanic ashes are found in parts of the early Tertiary sequence.

Interpretation: Supply of coarse sediment in the early Tertiary gave way to a supply of finer-grained material. The volcanic ashes suggest near-by explosive igneous activity, possibly in a northern extension of the Hebridean province to the west.

Western English Channel

Data: Several hundred metres of early Tertiary sediments, including limestones, pass up unconformably into over a hundred metres of later Tertiary sandy limestones.

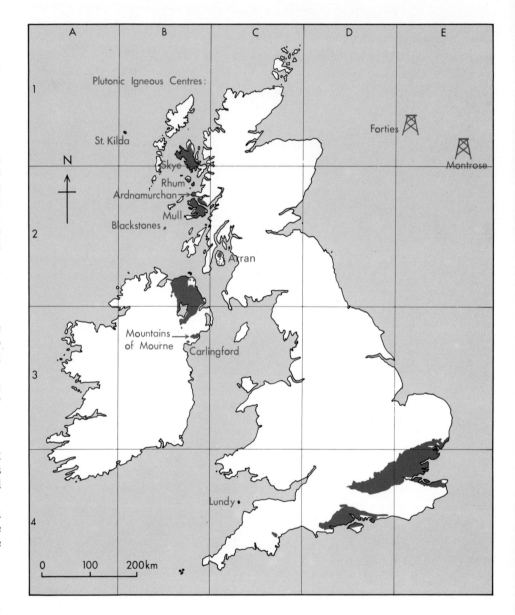

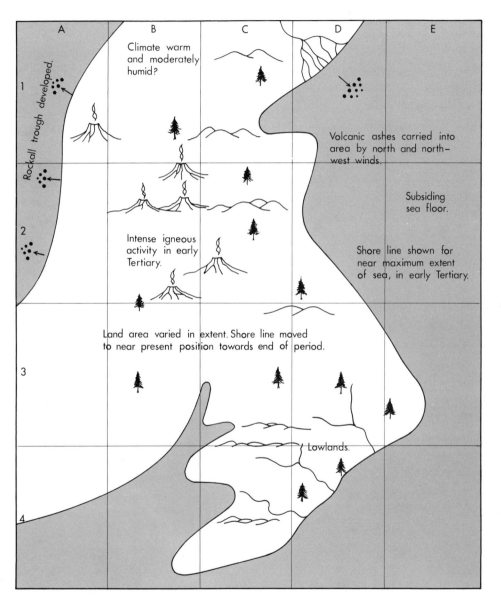

Within the figure:

A   B   C   D   E

1

Rockall trough developed.

Climate warm and moderately humid?

Volcanic ashes carried into area by north and north-west winds.

Subsiding sea floor.

2

Intense igneous activity in early Tertiary.

Shore line shown for near maximum extent of sea, in early Tertiary.

Land area varied in extent. Shore line moved to near present position towards end of period.

3

Lowlands.

4

Interpretation: There was periodic occupation of the area by shallow seas.

Palaeogeography

The sequence in southern England and the English Channel indicates that the sea withdrew markedly at the end of the Cretaceous, and for much of the Tertiary lay beyond the present-day shore line. In present-day offshore areas marine deposition continued, though intermittently in some regions. The extensive land exposed by the major **regression** (withdrawal) of the sea formed a source of sediment; relatively high land in north-east Scotland supplied sands for the early Tertiary deposits in the North Sea. In the north-west volcanic activity built extensive lava plateaux, fed either from fissures or from central volcanoes.

Continental drift and plate tectonics

The widespread igneous activity in the north-west of the British Isles is evidence of the formation of a major and persistent constructive margin. Both the volume and the predominantly basaltic type of igneous rock formed are compatible with this interpretation. The split led to the separation of areas that had been together since the Devonian; reconstruction of the continents to the pre-drift position makes sense of the similarities between so many of the Devonian to Tertiary sequences on land around the North Atlantic Ocean. The split did not take place exactly along the line of the convergence in the Palaeozoic, but along a line to the north-west of that, which is why there is in the British Isles today a remnant of 'North American' stratigraphy in north-western areas (see the Cambrian and Ordovician sections). Some geologists believe that the split began well before the Tertiary, as long ago as the Permian. Minor folds in southern England may be associated with a destructive margin or margins lying farther south, in the areas in which the Alpine orogeny was under way. The evidence of the fossil plants associated with some of the soil horizons interbedded with the early Tertiary lavas, and of the fossil fauna and flora in the early Tertiary sedimentary rocks in southern Britain, suggests a warmer climate than at present. This meshes with the palaeomagnetic evidence for a more southerly location of the British Isles at that time.

Economic

Early Tertiary sandstones in the North Sea contain important oil resources in fields such as Forties and Montrose; oil is also produced from early Tertiary chalk. On land, sand, gravel and mud are worked from the Tertiary in southern England. The igneous rocks of north-west Britain and north Ireland provide local sources of material for construction.

QUATERNARY

(about 2 million years ago to the present; named originally as the fourth great division of geological time)

Fossils

Plant spores are used both for dating and as indicators of climate. The Quaternary consists of the Pleistocene and Recent (Holocene) epochs. The Recent epoch covers only the last few thousand years, since the last retreat of the front of the Pleistocene ice sheets, which may advance again in the future in a geologically short period of time. Very late Pleistocene and Recent carbonaceous material can be dated by radiometric methods.

Areas of outcrop of special interest

Only marine deposits are shown on the outcrop map. Over large areas of the British Isles earlier rocks are concealed by non-marine Quaternary deposits:

Pleistocene All areas either have some evidence of highland or lowland glaciation or near glacier conditions. Marine beds are found in East Anglia.

Recent Sediments are found in all areas; this includes present-day river and coastal deposits, as well as peat.

England (East Anglia)

Data: Varied sediments, up to several tens of metres thick, contain some marine fossils; colder-water forms are commoner in the upper beds. These are overlain by up to one hundred metres of Pleistocene clays containing boulders of various types of rock.

Interpretation: A Tertiary sea already in the area persisted into the Pleistocene and became colder. Then ice sheets arrived, dumping unsorted sediments and erratic boulders, derived in some cases from distant sources. There were several advances and retreats of the ice front.

Highland areas of British Isles

Data: There are abundant U-shaped valleys, corries, knife-edge ridges, hanging valleys, **striated** (scratched) rock surfaces and rock-basin lakes; fjords are found on the west coast of Scotland; poorly sorted deposits of sand and gravel are widespread.

Interpretation: These areas were covered by ice sheets; mountains were sculptured, and preglacial watersheds were modified by **glacial breaching** as glaciers spilled over valley sides; **moraine** (glacial debris) was deposited at the front and sides of retreating glacier fronts and beneath glaciers; **rock-basin lakes** were scooped out of bedrock by ice and its debris; fluvio-glacial sands and gravels were laid down.

Lowland areas of British Isles

Data: Large areas of the British Isles are covered with unconsolidated and mainly poorly sorted sediments (**till**), over one hundred metres thick in places.

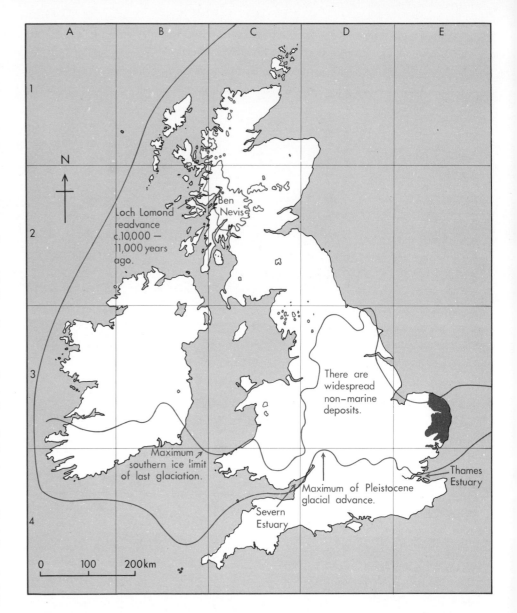

Eskers (sinuous ridges of sand and gravel), **kettle holes** (closed depressions), **drumlins** (streamlined hillocks in most cases composed of till), and **varves** (small scale annual alternations of silt and clay) are found. Many channels are cut into preglacial hill slopes and valley floors.

36

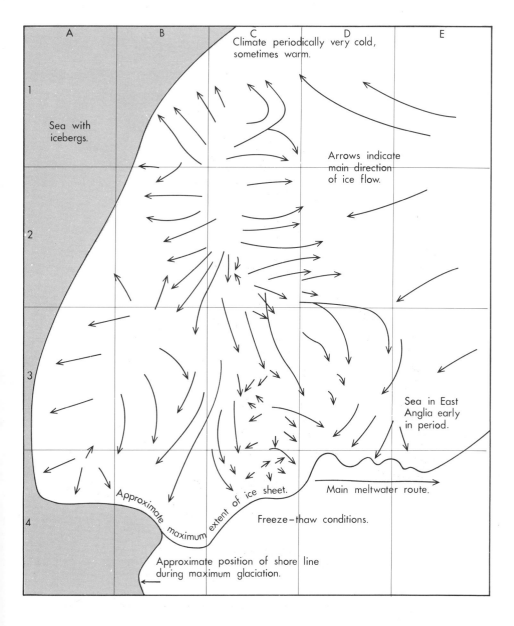

A B C D E

Climate periodically very cold, sometimes warm.

1

Sea with icebergs.

Arrows indicate main direction of ice flow.

2

3

Sea in East Anglia early in period.

Approximate maximum extent of ice sheet.

Main meltwater route.

Freeze–thaw conditions.

4

Approximate position of shore line during maximum glaciation.

Interpretation: Till was deposited from ice sheets, in places in the form of drumlins. Sediment-laden meltwater from the ice sheets formed sinuous ridges of sand and gravel beneath the ice, and in front of the leading edge. Channels carried away glacial meltwater from which sand and gravel outwash deposits

formed. In ice dammed lakes varves were formed, the silt from summer meltwaters, the clay during the winter. Melting of isolated blocks of ice formed kettle holes that in some cases still contain lakes.

Palaeogeography

The theoretical snowline at Ben Nevis is now at about 1600 metres. During glacial times it was lowered to about one thousand metres in all the main mountain areas of the British Isles, where ice sheets formed and spread into lowland areas. The fronts of the ice sheets advanced and retreated several times; times when ice sheets advanced were interrupted by times when the climate was less cold, including periods when it was as warm as or warmer than now. The farthest advance of the ice was to a line running roughly east–west from the Severn to the Thames estuary; even south of this line, as well as north of it, the effect of Pleistocene freeze–thaw conditions may be seen now. Since the last ice maximum about 17 000 years ago, there has been a general world-wide rise in sea level caused by the melting of the ice sheets; this has been more than counteracted locally by rises in land level caused by **isostatic rebounding** (bouncing back up) of the land following the removal of the great weight of the ice sheets. Evidence for this local uplift is found in parts of the British Isles in the form of raised shore lines.

Continental drift and plate tectonics

The British Isles had by now moved to their present latitude; the glaciations are evidence of a general refrigeration seen elsewhere, not of close approaches to the pole. Separation from North America continues at a few centimetres a year along the line of the constructive plate margin at the Mid-Atlantic Ridge. The 'Atlantic Ocean' has apparently opened and closed at least once before and may well do so at least once again.

Economic

Sands and gravels, both Pleistocene and Recent, are especially important in the construction industry. In south-east England these sources are limited, and here and elsewhere there is increasing interest in offshore dredging for Quaternary sand and gravel. The main impact of the ice age on present economic life is probably in farming, following the great erosion and deposition brought about by the ice sheets. The effect on scenery and land use is considerable; not only farming is involved, but also water supply, and access to mineral deposits in older rocks unconformably overlain by Quaternary material. The engineering work associated with the exploitation of North Sea and other offshore oil and gas necessarily takes heed of the most recent deposits on the sea floor which support the platforms and pipelines. On land, engineers need to consider both Pleistocene permafrost shattering of rocks and Pleistocene till when building foundations. Peat deposits are of more than local significance as a source of fuel in much of Ireland and are also used in parts of Scotland.

OUTCROP MAP OF THE BRITISH ISLES AND THE ADJACENT CONTINENTAL SHELF

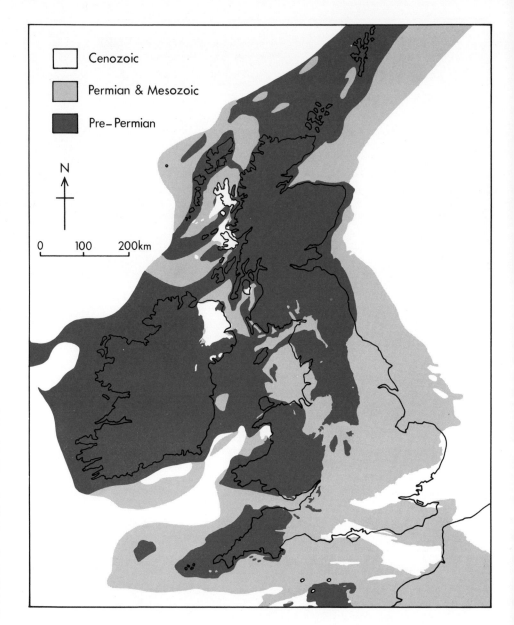

This map combines the land outcrop areas of the individual periods into larger groups, and in addition, gives information about offshore outcrop areas. It is an attempt to summarise information given in the preceding sections and to draw attention to some large scale features of the geology of the British Isles. Some of these large scale features are not necessarily clearly seen on the palaeo-geographical maps, because of the emphasis placed on distinguishing land from sea. While this emphasis is justified when considering major areas of erosion and deposition, it can in some cases obscure equally important long-term tectonic features.

This map is necessarily less detailed than those given for the individual periods. This is because offshore work is at a very early stage compared with onshore work and because much offshore stratigraphical work is carried out using geophysical methods which give only indirect evidence of the age of the rocks on and below the sea bed. Where boreholes have been put down, it is in most places possible to date the rocks using conventional palaeontological methods. A local stratigraphy can then be established and extrapolated.

The main features of the map may be listed as follows:

(1) There is a core of pre-Permian rocks in the north and west British Isles, broadly in the areas affected by the two major Palaeozoic orogenies, which remain the higher areas. The west and east margins of this core are, respectively, roughly parallel to the line of the late Mesozoic(?)–early Cenozoic separation of continents in the north-west, and to the main trend of Mesozoic–Cenozoic subsidence in the North Sea to the east.

(2) The Permian and Mesozoic strata surround this core and in places penetrate it. These are today mainly the lowland areas of the British Isles; most of any Mesozoic cover which existed on the higher Palaeozoic rocks has been removed by erosion.

(3) The surrounding Cenozoic rocks are mainly found offshore and form low ground onshore except for the igneous rocks of the north-west. Erosion rather than deposition predominated over most of the British Isles during much of the Cenozoic; the outcrop areas shown probably represent broadly the main depositional areas. The outcrop pattern in south-east England clearly links the rocks of this area with those of the North Sea.

By making allowances for the many phases of erosion and deposition that have affected the British Isles since the Carboniferous, it is possible to see in the outline of the present outcrop areas of the pre-Permian rocks the framework of the current outline of the British Isles. That this should be seen in the outcrop of rocks formed so long ago is less surprising if one remembers that the two major orogenies which affected the British Isles during the Phanerozoic and drastically changed their geography had already taken place by the end of the Permian. Only one event of the greatest importance remained; that was the separation of the continents in the north-west.

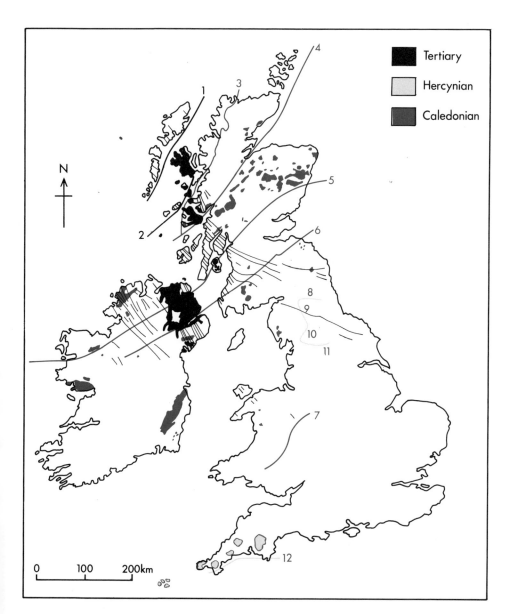

SUMMARY OF TECTONIC AND IGNEOUS ACTIVITY

Three major tectonic–igneous events may be identified in the Phanerozoic history of the British Isles:

Caledonian orogeny that took place mainly in the north-west of the British Isles in the middle Palaeozoic.
Hercynian orogeny that took place mainly in the south-west of the British Isles in the late Palaeozoic.
Tertiary igneous activity and faulting that took place mainly in the north-west of the British Isles.

The two orogenies were accompanied by folding with contrasting fold axial trends: broadly, north-east to south-west (Caledonian) and east to west (Hercynian). Crustal shortening and hence thickening took place not only by means of this folding, but also by **thrust faulting**, with the same trend as the folding, for example, the Moine Thrust (Caledonian) and the supposed Lizard–Dodman–Start Thrust (Hercynian) (in thrust faulting one crustal block moves over another on a nearly horizontal plane). These folds and thrusts resulted from compression; as discussed in the section on 'Continental drift and plate tectonics', attempts have been made to relate this compression to plate tectonics and continental drift, specifically to destructive plate margins and collisions between continents.

In at least the later stages of these two orogenies, two other types of faulting became important. There were faults with lateral movement on nearly vertical planes causing crustal blocks to move sideways relative to each other (such as the Caledonian Great Glen Fault) and **normal faults** with vertical or near

KEY TO FAULTS ON MAP

(1) Minch Fault
(2) Camasunary–Skerryvore Fault — Tertiary

(3) Moine Thrust
(4) Great Glen Fault
(5) Highland Boundary Fault — Caledonian
(6) Southern Uplands Fault
(7) Church Stretton Fault

(8) Stublick Fault
(9) Pennine Fault
(10) Dent Fault — Hercynian
(11) North Craven Fault
(12) Lizard–Dodman–Start Thrust(?)

Legend:
- Tertiary
- Hercynian
- Caledonian

vertical movement causing crustal blocks to move up and down relative to each other (such as the Caledonian Highland Boundary, Southern Uplands and Church Stretton Faults, and the Hercynian Stublick, Pennine, Dent and North Craven Faults). These normal faults are associated with tension. The normal Tertiary Minch and Camasunary–Skerryvore Faults may be related to tension associated with the opening of the present North Atlantic Ocean along a constructive plate margin.

It should be noted that many faults have a very long history, and may remain active for a long time, or be reactivated after a long time. The few faults cited as examples have here been associated with one tectonic event in which they are thought to have been significant; some of them were active before or after the time indicated.

Though both intrusive and extrusive igneous activity are often associated with orogeny, this is not necessarily the case. For example, much of the late Palaeozoic activity in Scotland followed the main Caledonian orogeny, while the Tertiary activity in the north-west was part of the process of formation of the North Atlantic Ocean. The relationship of igneous activity to plate tectonics is considered very briefly in the section dealing with 'Continental drift and plate tectonics'.

Only the intrusive granites and associated rocks emplaced in the roots of the Caledonian and Hercynian Mountains are shown on the map, while both the extrusive basalts and associated intrusive igneous rocks (note the long lines of the dyke swarms) are shown in the Tertiary province in the north-west. Other igneous rocks, mainly lavas, are included in the individual outcrop maps for each period. Many other intrusive igneous rocks, known to exist at depth, do not form outcrops and are not shown on this map.

INDEX OF TERMS DEFINED IN TEXT